M000079652

DON'T
LOOK BACK

14 June 2000

To: Monsieur Saulnier

Thanks for the help.

Patrick Oliver

Also by Patrick O'Connor

Poetry

NO POEM FOR FRITZ

Nonfiction

THE PRAYERS OF MAN, AN ANTHOLOGY

DON'T
LOOK BACK
A Memoir

PATRICK
O'CONNOR

MOYER BELL

WAKEFIELD, RHODE ISLAND & LONDON

Published by Moyer Bell

Copyright ©1993 by Patrick O'Connor

First Edition

LIBRARY OF CONGRESS
CATALOGING-IN-PUBLICATION DATA

O'Connor, Patrick, 1925-
    Don't look back: a memoir / by Patrick O'Connor.—
1st ed.
        p.   cm.
    Pieces originally written for "Lee Ryan's (only in) New York,"
WBAI-FM, New York, and previously published in various sources.
    ISBN 1-55921-098-2 : $16.95
    1. O'Connor, Patrick, 1925- —Anecdotes. 2. Publishers and
publishing—New York (N.Y.)—Anecdotes. 3. New York (N.Y.)—
Civilization—Anecdotes. 4. Theater—New York (N.Y.)—Anecdotes.
5. Book editors—New York, (N.Y.)—Anecdotes. I. Title.
Z473.029   1993   93-1054
070.5'092—dc20   CIP

Printed in the United States of America
Distributed by Publishers Group West, Box 8843, Emeryville, CA 94662,
1-800-788-3123 (in California 1-510-658-3453) (North America)
and by Gazelle Book Service (Europe)

Cover photo: Andrew A. Ciesielski

This book is for

Andrew A. Ciesielski

You are the sunshine of my life.

—Stevie Wonder

Contents

Acknowledgments

All of these pieces were originally written for "Lee Ryan's (Only In) New York," WBAI-FM, New York, still going strong, Sundays 6:30 P.M., 99.5 on your FM dial. So Lee Ryan is, indeed, the Godfather of this book and deserves my deepest thanks. There are a lot of others to thank: especially, two marvelous WBAI engineers: Tom Tortorella and Peter Cedric Smith who were patient and laughed at the right times.

When I first started to write these pieces I had the good luck to have a great editor, Norma McLain Stoop, and a lot of encouragement from a great friend, Mary Vaughan. Thanks are due once again to Lillian Gordon.

And thanks to Dick Courcelle who published "To Be a Ski Instructor" in *The Killington Magazine*, thanks also to Nick Russo who published it in *The*

Jungleer, the magazine of the 41st Infantry Division Association.

Most of the publishing pieces appeared in Leonore Fleischer's column "Talk of the Trade" in *Publishers Weekly*, and thanks Leonore for the suspenders. Anna Rose Johnson published the hometown stuff in her enchanting column "Kaleidoscope" in *The Free Press*, formerly *The Braddock Free Press*, and some of these pieces were published by Teresa Milewski in "The Show Dog Newsletter." "Showdog" is another word, and not a very nice one, for ski instructor.

Last but not least, thanks to my wonderful agent, Ruth Nathan, and her equally wonderful husband Paul who thought these slight pieces might make a book—we'll see.

DON'T
LOOK BACK

To Be a Ski Instructor
and Marry a Movie Star
and Other Such Fantasies

I suppose I wanted to be a ski instructor because when I was a boy ski instructors married movie stars. It's true. When the Jewish movie-producer husbands of movie stars died, their widows went to Sun Valley, where they married ski instructors named Eric and Rolfe, and their pictures appeared in the forbidden *Photoplay* or *Silver Screen*, tall handsome Scandinavians with peaked caps and pleated woolen knickers, holding ski poles with baskets the size of bicycle tires, staring into the sun and looking Godlike next to tiny little Norma Shearer photographed in front of the Sun Valley Lodge. So this is about wanting to marry a movie star, but I expect it to have a darker side.

When I was six my father, the coach, threw a ball at me, I dropped it. He laughed. I went to my room with my books and my bear and stayed there for forty years. It's pretentious to say I went to my room: I didn't have a room, but slept in the attic with the rest of the kids, the bear was imaginary, the books were real, my Aunt Rosie's. Hard to believe they were by Kathleen Norris, Faith Baldwin and Edna Ferber, some fare for a six year old. That's all there was in the house. My father was the soccer football coach of what is now called Carnegie Mellon and was then called Carnegie Tech—"Dear, old, Tech, Carnegie Tech you're the best of all the schools I ever knew." What time my father had off the field and out of the locker room he spent telling me what a klutz I was and how I couldn't do anything, and to get my nose out of that book.

I spent the next ten years, through adolescence, avoiding locker rooms, team sports and competition, anything involving a ball. I had my books and my bear. At sixteen I discovered the others who had spent their lives avoiding team sports and games with balls. We were above them and we made lots of jokes about dumb jocks but the laughter was hollow, very hollow.

In my fortieth year, I was visiting my friend Janice Weeks in Greenfield, Mass. In spite of Janice's passion for climbing, hiking, skiing, golf and tennis we were good friends. She played terrific bridge and had been known to read a book. Though I was unaware of it at the time it was a perfect ski weekend: sunshine and eight inches of fresh powder, I thought she was talking about Johnson's Baby Powder. We spent the first two days of the three-day weekend indoors, reading, tending the fire, listening to music, playing bridge, all the things I like to do. Finally the conditions got to Janice and she said, "I don't know about you but I'm going skiing and I want you to go with me." "Madame," I said, "I dwell in the cathedral of the mind, the New York Public Library is my natural home, you must be mad to think I would actually go out of doors on such a day." Yes, that pretentious.

She persisted and I said, "Very well, I'll go if you agree to carry everything and lace everything." Those were the days before buckled boots. She agreed. We got some funny looks in the base lodge of Mt. Snow when Janice knelt in front of me and laced my boots. And out to the slopes we went. I was furious: I hadn't had a drink, I hadn't read *The New York Times*, it was cold, the boots hurt. I could only think of P.G. Wodhouse who said, "There isn't enough trouble in the world that people have to put boards on their feet and slide down the sides of mountains." There we were, Janice and I, at the top of what I later realized was the smallest hill imaginable. I said "I'm going down." "No," she said, "You can't turn or stop or anything." "I'm going anyway," I said, hoping I would break my leg and end up

3

in the Brattleboro Hospital, where I could finally finish Proust.

The slope was as steep as a kitchen table. When I got to the bottom I was still standing. I was transfixed. I was Saint Paul on the road to Damascus. I was converted. I have, to this day, nothing to compare it with. At the end of the day, I was climbing up the side of this small hill in the dark over and over again and making my way down it as best I could. I had to be dragged off the slope by my friend Janice. I have been addicted to lots of things: cigarettes, booze, books, sugar but never anything like this. I gave up my booze and cigarette addiction so I'd be a better skier; I'm still working on sugar, and in spite of my father I never gave up books, I was totally hooked. With a singleness of purpose and a fury unlike any I had ever shown before about anything, I began to learn to ski. I was working for a publisher at the time, a nice man named Ivan Obolensky, and often I would call on Monday mornings and say I was stuck in Vermont, and often I was. Finally the nice publisher said, "Look you have to make up your mind. Do you want to work or ski?" I decided I would do a little freelance on the side and learn to ski. I not only became addicted to skiing but to ski school. I've been to many schools in many countries.

But in the beginning, since I was working in publishing, I had very little money so I was using Janice's long, long wooden skis with bear-trap bindings which she had used in college and which she had painted a bilious apple green so I could find them easily. And I used her brother Leon's boots that didn't fit and her brother's old ski clothes—they were made of gabardine and had pleats and I wish I had saved them. I transferred my allegiance to Hogback Mt. Ski School. In two years on these humongous skis I had barely mastered the snowplow turn. Unfortunately for Janice, fortunately for me, she had an automobile accident and a number of doctors told her no skiing. But she finally found a doctor who told her she could ski, but on short skis. We had been aware of short skis because a radical nut-case named Cliff Taylor had been teaching the short-ski method at Hogback Mt. Well, overnight my friend Janice became an expert skier and I threw the old apple-green boards away. On short skis I learned to turn and stop just like a real skier. Eventually the Killington Ski School used this method to revolutionize the teaching of skiing. Ah! Cliff Taylor, where are you today? We all owe you a great deal.

During the sixties in New York everyone I knew was getting a divorce and every recently divorced man feels guilty and poor. I did a lot of unprofessional counseling in those days and my advice to everyone was "Go to Killington and learn to ski." Always the same answer "Too old, can't afford it." And my answer "It's cheap and if I can do it anyone can." Half the CEO's in the publishing industry and their new families ski because of me. I could name names.

I figured if I could learn to ski I could learn to swim, catch a football, play softball. I asked to be on the Pinnacle Book Softball Team and they could hardly refuse me since I was the boss. I asked to play right field, the traditional sissy position. I knew so little about softball I went out to left field instead. Once I got there I knew I was in the wrong place. The rest of the team thought I was no good because I was fifty-five. Wrong, I was no good because I had never played before. When I finally got my first hit I was so astonished I forgot to run, but not the second time.

I had been skiing at Killington, Vt. for years and one year my friend Andy Ciesielski who is a ski instructor there was asked if he knew anyone who could help out on a crowded weekend. He gave them my name. I was appalled. The idea of a poet teaching ski-ing is mind boggling. The experience of combat in the infantry in World War II doesn't seem to wipe out the humiliation of not even being able to play right field as a teenager.

On my first day as a novice ski instructor I was asked to shadow a class and simply observe. The class I was "shadowing" was called the "Never-Evers": people who have never, ever been on skis before. It's where rookie instructors start. With the Never-Evers you don't do a lot of skiing, you teach them to put on their skis, make sure they're warm, try to dissipate their fears, teach them to walk on skis, a glide, a shift of weight and a stop and a turn if you're lucky, so not a lot of movement. Ski boots are not meant for walking and after walking around all day in 20° below weather, 40° below windchill factor, I was ready to cry. I've noticed over the years that sometimes really huge men don't have to hide their vulnerability behind a macho screen, Sylvester Stallone after all is practically a midget, so I said to the biggest man there, "I'm ready to cry," and he said "Me too." After that I felt better but I still felt that this wasn't for me. I was just about to say to nice guy Ed Robicheau, the head of the Never-Ever division of the ski school, that I couldn't possibly do this and he shouted "O'Connor, report for your uniform tomorrow." That did it. Dreams of glory. The image of myself married to Norma Shearer standing in front of the lodge at Sun Valley was enough. I would endure the boots that were not made for walking, 20° below cold. I would repeat to myself Martha Graham's mantra,

"Embrace the pain"; after all I am a Catholic, but I would be a ski instructor.

Now I'm not the kind of skier that flashes through your mind when you hear the words ski instructor: I'm short and fat and old and in spite of taking lessons everywhere in the world, I'm just an OK skier but, and it's a big but, I have total sympathy for the klutzes, the fatties, the uncoordinated and the fearful of the world, including Chinese ladies with bound feet and Pakistani ladies who have never been outdoors before. And one lady whose husband said to her just before he put her in ski school, "Selma, if you don't learn to ski I'm going to divorce your ass." I said to myself "Selma, I'll teach you to ski and then you can divorce that pig." I also see myself in each sixteen-year-old boy who's been brainwashed into thinking he wasn't athletic. And every girl who has been brainwashed into thinking it's a man's sport—in fact women are easier to teach than men. So I'm doing God's work—anybody who teaches anybody to do anything is doing God's work, and anybody who teaches a klutz to ski is going to get the brightest crown in heaven. And, of course, I'm finally in my father's locker room.

Donald Duck

I was hired to ghostwrite a book on skiing or more properly rewrite a book on skiing long before I knew much of anything about skiing which tells you more about the book business than you ought to know. What happened was an impressionable, young New York editor fell in love with her Vermont ski instructor and offered him a contract to write a book. An unintelligible scribbled manuscript came in written on the back of cocktail napkins and match book covers. Unfortunately a great title had already been decided on, the cover designed, the book was featured in the publisher's catalog and the salesmen were out selling the book, but no book. I was hired to fix it up including the introduction by a then-famous movie star and the price was right. It was exactly the sum of a piano I had been longing for. It was a rush job. I took all the ski books out of the library, very few in those days, and read back issues of *Ski* and *Skiing* magazines but there wasn't time to do much research the manuscript was due yesterday. I set up the skis and boots in my living room and would work out a maneuver and then rush to the bedroom where the old Remington typewriter was set up, try and remember the moves and write about them. This was summer in Manhattan in a nonair-conditioned, walk-up, semislum apartment with the temperature in the nineties, so naturally I didn't have any clothes on.

Every afternoon around five a messenger would come and pick up a new chapter so that it could be copyedited, proofread and put in the works, this was really a rush job. I was making progress, I wrote about a chapter a day and when the messenger came I always managed to throw a towel around myself for propriety's sake.

Of course, I smoked, everyone smoked in those days especially free lance writers. My friend Hubert Saal, at the time the music critic of *Newsweek* and I used to discuss giving up smoking but we agreed that typewriters couldn't be made to work without cigarette smoke. We decided that after we gave up smoking we would hire some poor indigent to come to the office and blow smoke into the typewriter while we worked, the same man, presumably I'm going to hire to swim for me every day when I win the lottery.

One morning I woke unable to breathe and there were five crumpled up, empty packages of unfiltered Pall Mall cigarettes on the desk. I knew something had to be done. The previous summer there had been a family reunion in Braddock, Pa. and my smart sister Nancy had brought her beautiful daughter Linda all the way from California. Linda sucked her thumb and when the aunts clucked-clucked and suggested that a little girl Linda's age shouldn't be sucking her thumb my sister Nancy said "You smoke don't you."

I went to the drugstore and bought five pacifiers. Alas the only ones available had Donald Duck on the other end, nothing daunted I took them home. It worked: every time I wanted a cigarette which when you're writing is every minute you're at the typewriter I chomped down on the Donald Duck pacifier. I went through three that day but I got through the day and the chapter without a cigarette. At five o'clock, on time, the messenger rang the doorbell. Now, New York City messengers are not exactly Rhodes scholars but when I opened the door and he saw a sweaty, naked man (I had forgotten to put a towel around me) sucking on a Donald Duck pacifier he knew that something very funny was going on in that apartment.

Incidentally, one of the most beloved and popular novels ever written was illegibly scribbled on the back of cocktail napkins and empty matchbook covers and put together by a genius editor but that's all the clues you'll get out of me.

That Contraption

My baptismal name is Robert, my confirmation name is Patrick and I was called Bob by my friends and Bobby by my mother and my Aunt Rosella. I came to New York in 1952, having been the director of the Rochester Arena Theater of which I was one of the cofounders and before that a theater in Adrian, Michigan. A friend, Arthur Conescu, preceded me to New York by two years and he had a glamorous and wonderful job working for a high-powered agent at M.C.A. which was then the hot talent agency. My friend said I could have the job if I wanted it, no interview—nothing. I taught myself typing and shorthand (if u cn rd ts u cn rn mr mnee). The job was as an assistant, read secretary, to Robert Sanford, he was called Bobby; he was the first one in New York to call people darling, sweetheart, the first real babytalker.

I got the job and went to work on July 2 in the plush offices of M.C.A. I had been sitting at my desk for ten minutes and the phone rang, the woman at the other end said "Bobby?" and I said "Yes," wondering how my mother who didn't even know I had left Rochester had found me so quickly. The voice, one of the most singular voices of the twentieth century, was the voice of Marlene Dietrich and she thought she was talking to her agent Bobby Sanford. She sailed right in. It was clear that Yul was Yul Brynner and she was having an affair with him and they were making love (not at all the expression she used) in a small apartment in Manhattan without air-conditioning in the middle of summer. The apartment had no ventilation, it looked out on an airshaft. She then proceeded to describe in vivid and graphic detail the variations Mr. Brynner was able to bring to the activities. I once in a while shouted into the phone "But Miss Dietrich, sir." She was unstoppable.

Finally after a blow-by-blow retelling of the entire incident she simmered down and I got through to her. I said "But Miss Dietrich you're talking to the wrong Bobby." She slammed the receiver down. At this point I had been working for Mr. Sanford for twenty-five minutes. I went into his office and told him what happened and said I understood if he would have to let me go. He said "What's your name son?" and I said "Robert O'Connor." He said "Do you have a middle name" and I said "Yes, Patrick." Bobby Sanford was one of those people who when they see an "O" in front of someone's name immediately goes into a stage Irish brogue and this was no exception. He said "Patrick me boyo I'll see if I can't straighten it out with the Kraut"— he called her the Kraut behind her back, and sometimes to her face—"but if you're going to work for me your name is Patrick from now on." Well I should have quit but I didn't. I would like to find Mr. Sanford's grave and drive a spike through his heart for giving me two names.

Bobby Sanford, like many New Yorkers, was only interested in one thing, getting away to the country; he would have gone on Monday afternoon if he thought he could get away with it but the best he could do was Thursday at noon. Just before he left for the fourth of July weekend he said "Patrick me boyoo, you're going to have to service the Kraut over the weekend." I wasn't exactly sure what he meant and given what I already knew about Miss Dietrich I hoped his metaphor "service" was not drawn from the farm. It meant, he explained, that I had to pick her up, take her to a taping, take her out for a meal if she wanted one and then take her home. I later realized that it took a lot of chutzpah for Mr. Sanford not to be at the taping since it was the first taping of an enormously expensive new radio show called CAFE ISTANBUL in which Miss Dietrich was the host and leading actress. ABC ever on the cutting edge decided that TV was a passing fad and they were wisely going to put all their money into radio. They would have called the show "A Night at Rick's" or "Casablanca" if they thought they could get away with it but that was the idea. I was told to pick her up at 6:00 P.M. I went to her apartment on Park Avenue in the sixties, the doorman sent me up without phoning and I rapped on her door—no answer. I rapped, I banged I thought, my God I have the wrong night, I panicked. I went downstairs, the doorman said "She'll answer when she's ready. Just go up and wait." I waited. Finally she appeared. She didn't look at me or speak to me. She looked magnificent: She had on a dark suit made of some sort of sharkskin that's usually used for men's suits but this material was softer. It was brilliantly cut with a touch of white at the throat; black patent leather shoes with gray kidskin and little black pearl buttons; an enchanting though simple hat (Lili Dache?), black kid gloves. She had one other item of apparel about which my memory plays tricks; it wasn't a fur, she would never have worn a fur in July. It wasn't a coat, again too hot, and it wasn't a raincoat. It might have been a black boa, I had probably never seen one before, later in the evening she gave it to me to hold and I clutched it like a drowning man holding onto a life preserver but I still don't remember what it was. The doorman couldn't find a cab, I couldn't find a cab —panic—finally I found one on Madison and brought it round. This was before the days of the stretch limos. We got in the cab and I handed her her mail; one letter was from Adlai Stevenson (handwritten), the other was from Hemingway (typed) and though she didn't speak one word to me or look at me I was in orbit.

We arrived at ABC, she handed me the thing, we'll call it a boa, and she went to work. Within minutes I could see that she was the consummate professional. She listened carefully to the director, she took the direction she thought made sense and rejected that which didn't. She was courteous to all and she worked with a kind of fierce energy I had never seen before yet she somehow remained cool and glamorous. I just sat in a corner being as unobtrusive as possible. Halfway through the proceedings she looked in my direction but not at me, wiggled her finger and I went over to her. She said without looking at me "Pastrami on rye no mustard, black coffee." That's all she said but I picked up my cue fast enough. When I returned she took the pastrami and the coffee and handed me the two slices of rye which I disposed of. Still no eye contact. Things were winding down and I was nervous about what was going to happen; should I ask her if she would like to go out, should I ask her if she wanted me to take her home. I stood there with this thing in my hand feeling very ill at ease.

Lurking around had been what I later learned were three ABC vice presidents, all in sharkskin and the '52 equivalent of Gucci loafers, white-on-white shirts, Countess Mara ties and pocket handkerchiefs. They were lined up in a row and one timorously said "Miss Dietrich may we take you out for a little supper?" She looked at them for what seemed a long while and then turned to me and looked me in the eye for the first time, turned back to the phalanx of VP's, swept me up if such a thing can be said to have happened and said as we walked out the door: "You may join us but I am with Patrick."

We went to a club called Roger Stern's 1,2,3. I was her escort. We walked in, heads turned. We were seated, the three VP's opposite, Miss Dietrich and I were sitting side by side on the banquette. Now these guys were your regular $100,000 per year ABC VP's. They knew I was from her agency and though they didn't know I made $35.00 per week they knew I wasn't top of the heap. After drinks were ordered she turned

asked what she thought of Dietrich. She said scorn-
fully "That contraption."

Ah, but what a magnificent contraption.

On the Street of Dreams

Anita Helen Brooks is not a typical New Yorker, she is the quintessential New Yorker. She could be anywhere from sixty to eighty, as blonde as the peroxide bottle will allow, straight as a pencil and slim as an Indian brave. Like many New Yorkers she has done a lot of things, and married a lot of people. After graduating from Hunter College she was a Latin teacher, an actress and God knows what else but since I've known her she has been a press agent, the quintessential New York profession. She's a hustler and she's hustled everything from the Duchess of Windsor to a beauty parlor called, if you'll believe it, the Apex La Dainty. She wears those Joan Crawford spike heels and flashy clothes and though she doesn't chew gum the effect is the same: When I hear those heels clicking behind me I know I'm in for a hustle of something.

Once I was having trouble getting an interview in a magazine called *Publishers Weekly* for one of my authors, Helen Van Slyke by name, no mean hustler herself, but with no luck. The might of CBS couldn't seem to manage it but Anita Helen Brooks did. Years later I asked Arnold Ehrlich, the editor of the magazine in question and subsequently the editor of *Town and Country*, how Anita managed to get the interview. He said "Hell, I'd give her the whole magazine just to get her off the phone."

Among other things Anita is always hustling a restaurant and about once a year she wears me down and I agree to have lunch with her. We were having lunch in one of her places, I forget which one or I would plug it for her, and I was eavesdropping on the dwarf and the regular-sized person at the next table while Anita droned on about the Duchess of Windsor or some such. By the way Anita has managed to hustle her way in to Burke's Peerage, go figure.

I've raised eavesdropping to a fine art and I'd never eavesdropped on a dwarf's conversation before so I was concentrating hard when suddenly Anita said "You know Patrick I used to date the King of Yugoslavia." I said "No" and then Anita said "Yes, I used to date the King of Yugoslavia but kings don't mean a thing to me." She actually said it. I thought the dwarf would fall off his chair. And I got her to say it three more times. I said "Is it true Anita that kings don't mean a thing to you" and she said it again. "That's right Patrick, kings don't mean a thing to me." So here's a birthday salute on Bastille Day or thereabouts to Anita Helen Brooks a lady to whom kings don't mean a thing.

Lying for Lucia

In nineteen fifty-five I was given a copy of *All About Lucia* by a friend Edward Fenton, the distinguished writer of childrens books. I read it, alas, in one gulp, the young are so greedy. And when I was finished I realized I had found what I had been looking for: a replacement in my life for the Roman Church. The *Lucia* novels have been a sheltering rock through stormy years. Years later, a friend Alec Wilder, the composer, said "Unlike the Bible the *Lucia* novels contain all wisdom."

At the time I was a television producer, mostly sports shows, so I had no thoughts that *Lucia* should be on television. The books had been originally published in the States in the twenties by Doubleday and were scarce as hen's teeth. O'Malley's, a great second-hand bookstore run by two Irish brothers on Fourth

25

Avenue in New York City, kept a list of names on a piece of foolscap and at the top of the foolscap it said in large block letters WILL PAY ANYTHING FOR LUCIA NOVELS and here are the folks who were on the list: Noel Coward, Gertrude Lawrence, Cyril Ritchard, Bella Spewack ("Kiss Me Kate"), John Van Druten, W.H. Auden, Patrick O'Connor. Mine was the only name I didn't recognize.

The most sought-after edition was entitled *All About Lucia* which contained *Queen Lucia, Lucia in London, Miss Mapp* and *Mapp and Lucia* with an introduction by Gilbert Seldes and a foreword by Anne Parrish. I've only ever seen three copies of that particular edition; the one that was given to me by my friend Fenton, another given to me by my friend Seymour Palestin and last year I bought a third copy at Powell's Bookstore in Portland, Oregon (the best bookstore in the world). I cried when I saw it and paid eight dollars for it but I would have paid three hundred dollars if asked.

All About Lucia is a handy volume you can take to bed with you whereas the big HarperCollins *Make Way for Lucia* is big enough for a doorstop and quite unhandy.

The saga of getting the *Lucia* novels republished in the U.S. requires a short course in American book publishing but there are a few laughs along the way and I'll make it as painless as possible.

I left wretched television and started at the very bottom of the book business at the late age of thirty-five. I was at the wrong end of the totem pole for about eight years, doing other peoples' dirty work but I always had the *Lucia* books in my office, waiting for the moment to strike.

I was working at New American Library as a senior editor in the late sixties and could occasionally push a book through for publication in spite of my relative inexperience. In order for an editor to get the go-ahead to publish a book the editor had to get not only the approval of, first, an editorial board (easy, I had converted the entire editorial staff to *Lucia*) but the approval of what was called the "publishing board," consisting of the President, Sales Manager, Publicity Person, Rights Manager, in other words the nonreading brass, the money people.

I carried the books around with me for a year, they began to look like an extension of my arm. Sometimes the publishing board meeting which started in the morning would run overtime and we would have to break for lunch and sometimes, especially in the summertime, some of these men from whom I was desperately trying to extract the money to buy the rights

27

to these books would come back from lunch having had a few cool cups on a summer's day and fall asleep. One day they were all asleep except for the secretary of the meeting, a wonderful man named Robert Haynie who was an editor and on my side. I went through my pitch (very like the movie pitch one reads about these days), the sleepy board nodded, the secretary recorded their approval and *Lucia* was about to be republished in the U.S. of A.

The next morning, the President, a nice guy named Herb Schnall, said, "I think you put one over on us O'Connor, these books better earn their money." The advance was minuscule.

When I die and go to heaven God is going to say "Yes, you can stay in the paperback business but you never have to go to another cover (art) meeting." It's the meeting at which the cover painting and design are decided. If there are ten people at the meeting there are ten art directors all with a different opinion. If you've wondered why sometimes on the covers of paperback books the heroine is blonde when clearly in the novel she is a brunette, that's where it's done—at the cover meeting. Editors, including this one, have been known to scream hysterically "Could we just get the hair color right, just once?" My friend Frances Rickett recently had a book published and on the cover was an illustration of a mother and a daughter. Frances called me up in tears to say that the whole point of her book was that the heroine never had a mother. Rarely does anything good or even satisfactory come out of a cover meeting.

The covers of the New American Library editions (a Signet Novel, 1971) of the *Lucia* books were not bad, Edwardian pastoral and quite pretty but totally unrelated to the text. The cover of *The Worshipful Lucia* looked like a book of ornithology. I took a Nancy Mitford review and bludgeoned her agent into letting me chop it up and use it as an introduction. (Poor Miss Mitford. Years later knowing she needed the money I bludgeoned her agent into letting me publish her early novels as original paperbacks in the U.S.; novels she didn't like and didn't feel should be republished.) I did everything I could to promote the *Lucia* books except stand on my head in Times Square, and I would have done that if I thought it would help.

They sank without a trace. I think we got more copies back than we printed, in fact I know we did. At the time some smart book wholesaler was manufacturing covers and sending them back for full credit (sophisticated thievery). I told you you would learn more about the U.S. book business than you could ever want to know. I was not fired but there were some dark glances in my direction.

It was all worthwhile, however. I got a letter in the mail which even as I write is framed and on my bathroom wall. Here is the letter in full: "Dear Mr. O'Connor, As a devoted *Lucia* fan for many years you can imagine how delighted I am to see that they are now going to be available at a cheap price. Thank you so much. Yours sincerely, W.H. Auden.

"Well," I said to myself "that was obviously the wrong way to publish these books. What these books need is a distinguished hardcover publication." I never give up, I've now published *A Dance to the Music of Time* by Anthony Powell twice without success.

Eventually the rights to publish *Lucia* reverted from New American Library to the estate of E.F. Benson (N.A.L was glad to get rid of them) and I eventually left N.A.L. but not over the *Lucia* books.

I moved to Popular Library, another paperback publishing house (owned by CBS) as editor in chief and immediately acquired all U.S. *Lucia* rights (hardcover and soft) for very little money. This time, I said, I'm going to do it right.

I set about finding a powerful editor in a hardcover house who would be sympathetic to the *Lucia* cause and give the books (in one volume, I thought best) a distinguished hardcover publication which I could not do, since Popular Library was a paperback publisher only. I was not the brass and had a decent expense account and could wine and dine editors and expose them to the one true faith.

Finally I found a young man named Nick Ellison who is now a powerful agent but was then an unpowerful editor, at T.Y. Crowell. He loved the books, he also liked good food and fine wines. As much as he enjoyed the attention and the frequent excursions to four-star restaurants he was an honest gent and finally said to me after too many free meals, "Look, I work for a very tough guy named Lew Gillenson, and if you think he's going to allow me to publish six novels in one volume about life in rural England by the faggot son of the Archbishop of Canterbury, you're crazy." Undeterred I then told THE LIE. "But Nick, these books are going to be on Masterpiece Theater next season." This was 1977. He said "No kidding?" I said "No kidding." Nick Ellison went back to his boss with THE LIE lie and the deed was done.

The books came out in one volume under the title *Make Way for Lucia*, a name I stole from a play by John Van Druten which he adapted from the books and which had a brief run on Broadway with Cyril Ritchard and Isobel Jeans. The one-volume edition was a smash. *Lucia* became a bestseller and was in every bookstore in the U.S. It got an ecstatic front-page review in *The New York Times*, and lead reviews in *Time*, *Newsweek*, etc. One reviewer, Bill Cole of *The Saturday Review* said that the only reason the books were being revived was because of the upcoming Masterpiece Theater TV production. In fact, everyone who reviewed the books mentioned Masterpiece Theater, and every time it was mentioned I felt like crawling under my desk and hiding.

T.Y. Crowell, the hardcover publisher, was ecstatic, my bosses at Popular Library were thrilled— we owned the paperback rights. The T.Y. Crowell hardcover edition came out in 1977 and books were published by Popular Library separately in paperback with, at last, decent, covers in 1978 and everything was hunky dory as they say. When the Popular Library book salesmen kept asking me about the Masterpiece Theater TV production what could I do but agree with them, after all they had read about it in *Time* magazine.

One day, while sitting at my desk, my secretary, Mary Ployardt indicated there was a phone call for me. "It's Masterpiece Theater on the phone for you" she said. "Mr. O'Connor," the angry, authoritative voice of an outraged woman at the other end of the line said "We have traced this lie to you." She let me have it pretty good. With a few "How dare you's" and "You have a lot of nerve" etc. And after letting me have it for about twenty minutes she started to laugh and said "Now that these books have been brought to our attention we are quite interested in them." Which led my friend James Elward to say "There are no lies. There are only truths that haven't happened yet."

Eventually *Lucia* came to the U.S. on Public Television and was a smash, though some of us were quite huffy about what had been done to the sacred text. No movie, television show or play could ever satisfy a true Luciaphile.

Eventually T.Y. Crowell was bought by Harper & Row, now HarperCollins, and HarperCollins owns all U.S. rights and they are the current publisher. Happily they keep the books in print both in the omnivolume *Make Way for Lucia* and the individual volumes. They continue to sell incredibly well, they are all, all of them, always in bookstores everywhere in the U.S., both the omnibus volume which contains *The Male Impersonator* which was supplied to me by the greatest Luciaphile of them all, Edward Gorey, and the single-volume editions.

There was an active Miss Mapp Society (named by Andrew Ciesielski) with an enormous board and only one member, and lots of squabbling. The large board didn't find anyone up to their standards. Finally the organization was wrested away from the board by me and Marjorie Mortenson who sparkplugged the organization for years. She did all the work, I got all the glory. Miss Mortenson got bored doing all the work and I moved to Vermont to be a ski instructor. So at the moment the Miss Mapp Society is moribund.

Alan Rich, a New York music critic, once told me he was in the hospital at death's door and someone brought him the new Popular Library editions of the *Lucia* books. He had read them before and was delighted to get them but what saved his life by making him laugh was a note in the front of the book which I'm proud to say I wrote "Though the character Lucia does not appear in the novel *Miss Mapp*, nevertheless *Miss Mapp* has always been known as a "Lucia" novel and is, in fact, volume III in the series. Mapp is furious."

My Affair
with Ayn Rand

Permanent pockets in a bookstore is what every writer longs for or should; let me explain: when you go to a paperback bookstore to buy your monthly copy of Danielle Steele you take it out of a space which in the trade is known as a pocket; behind the one you took is yet another Danielle Steele. When the pocket is empty the bookstore owner does not replace it with the new Harold Brodky, he replaces it with the new Danielle Steele. It's called having a permanent pocket and very few American writers have permanent pockets but you can guess which ones have: Stephen King, Tom Clancy, Dean Koontz, the list is limited. Ayn Rand had permanent pockets for years and with these permanent pockets she paid the gas, light, rent, telephone bills and, more important, Christmas bonuses for New American Library, her paperback publisher.

One day Ayn (rhymes with mine) Rand invited the brass of N.A.L. (the President and all the little vice presidents) to her apartment (Thirty-fourth and Third Avenue, New York City) for dinner. After dinner she lined them like schoolboys and asked "Tell me gentlemen, which one of my books did you like best and why?"

Not one of these gentlemen, distinguished publishing types all, had read one word of one of her books. The President of N.A.L., a cultured man who regularly read *The New York Times Book Review*, tried to fake it. No cigar. You didn't fake it with Miss Rand.

When I was told the story I didn't think it was very funny. Watch out. I get a little pompous here. If a book sells over seven hundred and fifty thousand copies (my arbitrary number) in paperback it contains a secret. I firmly believe that almost any book given the proper amount of money can be hyped up to seven hundred and fifty thousand copies. In other words with enough publicity, promotion and advertising you could promote almost anything—though perhaps not a book by Ronald Reagan. But beyond that arbitrary number a book contains a secret that makes people say to each other "You must read this book." Or in my case "If you don't read this book I'll never speak to you again." Which is why in the past you could have found me in a bookstore leafing through Jacqueline Susann and currently someone named Sandra Brown.

I had read all of Ayn Rand's books looking for the secret and had found it. She was, and perhaps still is, the best writer of young adult books in America. Before I was in the book business I met one of her disciples and told the disciples to tell Miss Rand just that.

When I told my bosses at N.A.L. that I had read all her books they said "You're her editor." I said "No I couldn't possibly be her editor, the woman's a fascist." We talked that way in the sixties. The President said "OK smart-ass. You read the books, you're her editor."

I called Miss Rand up to tell her that I had been assigned to be her editor, underlining the word "assigned," and made a date with her for lunch at the Copenhagen Restaurant, Fifty-eighth and Sixth Avenue, New York City.

When I arrived she was already seated at the table. I sat down and the first thing I said to her was "Miss Rand the first thing you must know about me is that I'm a Trotskyite." Miss Rand said in that thick Russian accent "Mr. O'Connor it doesn't matter about your politics as long as you are good editor and do everything I say." I did everything she said for the next few years.

I firmly believe that when a writer like Ayn

Rand sells as many copies as she did she has certain rights and I saw to it that she got them. When I went back after the lunch and reported to my bosses that she was just a little old Jewish lady from Leningrad they wouldn't believe me.

Miss Rand and I fell into each other's arms; we became good friends. I got a couple of books out of her based on material from her newsletter. I thought her politics were lunatic and her economic theories were from Disneyland but I found her to be compassionate, warm hearted, caring and a good companion. We never discussed politics.

I took her and her husband to the ballet and the theater and we had lots of long dinners and lunches. We poured out our hearts to each other and became intimate friends.

Slyly she once asked me if I was the Mr. O'Connor who said she wrote the best juveniles in America and I had to confess that I was but she never mentioned it again.

At the time I was in analysis (when wasn't I) with the woman who saved my life Lillian Gordon, another short conservative Jewish lady, and needless to say I used to talk about Miss Rand. One day I happened to mention that Miss Rand's married name was O'Connor and my analyst said "Thank God you told me." I said why and she said "One day you'll be out of here and one day I'll be reading Miss Rand's obituary and see that she was also a Mrs. O'Connor and I'll think, my God, he married her."

Mrs. Roosevelt

When Eleanor Roosevelt was the first lady she
kept a little apartment on Washington Square West and
people who lived in the neighborhood at the time tell
me that when she went to the theater she went alone to
the West Fourth St. stop of the Independent, rode the
subway to 42nd St. and Sixth Ave. and then walked to
the theater. I've never read this but I've heard it often
enough. Recently, I was talking to the son of one of
Roosevelt's leading cabinet members and I asked him
if it were true. I happened to know that this man's mother was a Hyde Park friend of Mrs. Roosevelt. He said
"It was absolutely true, my mother used to say 'Surely,
Eleanor, we could take a taxi?' And Mrs. Roosevelt
would say 'Subway's good enough.'" And away they'd
go, the wife of the President of the United States and
the wife of Secretary of the Treasury Morgenthau into

the Sixth Ave. Subway off to the theater, unaccompanied. The idea of the President's wife riding the subway alone makes one yearn for those days and makes me want to take an ax to every stretch limo I see. It is my own opinion that the French Revolution was caused by the stretch limo or at least the stretch limo of the day—the closed carriage.

I told this story to Michael Thomas, and he said: "Despite her politics it proves that she was well brought up."

So how about Mrs. Bush on the subway? Probably. Mrs. Carter? Probably. Mrs. Onassis? Probably except for the papparazzi. Mrs. Reagan? Not on your life.

Playbills

      I first came to New York from Braddock, Pa., on a visit during Christmas week of nineteen forty-three when I was sixteen. Braddock is not a middle-class suburb of Pittsburgh but a mean, dirty mill town. Nevertheless I was theater-mad and a dance nut and to me New York was mecca. My family was poor but I was a hustler: I sold ice skates at the Honus Wagner Sporting Goods Store in downtown Pittsburgh, called bingo at the local K of C and sold more copies of the *Saturday Evening Post* than anyone in western Pennsylvania. So I really had more money than my father though I was only sixteen. When I told my parents I wanted to go to New York for Christmas they said, "No," but in my family money talked so they let me go.

      It was agreed that I would stay with my Uncle

James and his family in Bay Ridge, Brooklyn (then as now a middle-class suburb of New York). My uncle was the most sophisticated man I knew. He wore a coat and tie to work and he worked in the New York office of Lloyds of London, not only had he been to the theater but he had been to an opera. He had a daughter and three sons: Frances, Jimmy, Tommy and Raymond. My cousin Frances was a student at Hunter College and was somewhat aware of what I thought of as the great world, in other words, music, theater, dance and art, but my male cousins were, to my horror, Brooklyn Dodger fanatics, and sports nuts. They were the first people I'd ever heard express the opinion that Manhattan was not the most wonderful place in the world and if they could avoid it they did. A shocking opinion since I had never been there but had planned to spend my life there, which I have.

My Uncle James asked me what I'd like to do while I was in New York and I started reeling it off: Gypsy Rose Lee and Bobby Clark in *Star and Garter*, Tallulah Bankhead and the Marches in *The Skin of Our Teeth*, Judith Anderson, Katherine Cornell and Ruth Gordon in *The Three Sisters*. Just as my cousins knew every baseball player in the world and their batting averages I knew every cast member in every Broadway play and their understudies, plus who was dancing what,

43

when, and where, though admittedly there was not much dance at the time, or not enough for me at any rate.

My uncle said "Hold on young man, everything you mention is highly unsuitable according to the *Brooklyn Tablet*," which was and still is for all I know the Brooklyn diocesan newspaper. "Your cousin Frances will take you to see Ruth Draper." My Uncle James didn't go to see *Oklahoma* because he suspected that Alfred Drake was a communist—not true. Politically my uncle was to the right of Attila the Hun and anticipated Joe McCarthy by twenty years. Except for his politics he was a nice man, he lived to be ninety-five and we remained friends.

It was odd that I had never heard of Ruth Draper but I hadn't. I guess Harold V. Cohen of the *Pittsburgh Post Gazette* didn't like her because he never mentioned her. His column was my bible. Ruth Draper was wonderful and the audience was even more wonderful. Behind Frances and me were two very elegant gentlemen and their conversation made me dizzy: They had been everywhere, Paris, London, Rome. At some point in discussing a mutual friend one said to the other "But you must admit that he's very cultured." "Well, it's a sort of dancing school culture," the other replied. Smart New York talk, I was enchanted. It took me five years to realize that those gents were not father and son and no better than they should be.

My cousin Tommy took me to Radio City Music Hall and even then I wasn't impressed. I wanted art with a capital A and culture and though I didn't know the word I recognized kitsch when I saw it. After the show we went to the Spaulding Company to look at baseball bats. I convinced my cousin Tommy I could find my way back to Bay Ridge.

To set me free in Manhattan was a wicked and courageous thing for him to do but I've been grateful to him for doing it ever since. I hotfooted it to the box offices of various theaters and got tickets to *Star and Garter*, *The Skin of Our Teeth*, *The Three Sisters* and practically everything else that was playing at the time.

Going to the theater was no problem I simply said I had been to the movies (eccentrics learn to lie early), careful to mention only movies approved by the Legion of Decency.

Years later in a course I took with Walter Kerr at Catholic University he discussed censorship and mentioned the very season I had first been in New York and he said that a conscientious Catholic in the season '42-'43 could only go to see *Howdy, Mr. Ice!* which is precisely what my Uncle James had suggested.

So I said I went to the movies twice a day. No problem relating the plot, I was an early reader of *Variety*.

There was one almost insurmountable problem. How to save the playbills without getting caught. They were as valuable as seeing the show. To be pored over in the attic when I got back to Braddock and for the delectation and envy of the two friends in my high school class who were theater nuts too. They would never believe me unless I could show proof.

On the first matinee day I'd rush back to Brooklyn for dinner and then back to New York for another movie (read play). During dinner I regaled them with the plot of the movie I supposedly had seen in the afternoon. My uncle relieved me of this burden when he told me the second most sophisticated thing I had heard till then. New Yorkers don't come back, they stay in town and they eat out. I had never eaten out. Ah, the beans and brown bread at the Automat.

My biggest problem was what to do with the playbills. Hide them in the suitcase? No. Going to see Gypsy Rose Lee produced not only guilt but paranoia. I was sure someone would go through my suitcase and find out what I was up to. Going to see forbidden Gypsy Rose Lee was not the only thing this Catholic boy was guilty and paranoid about.

It was winter and I was wearing a great big overcoat. Though I was a Depression child and felt as though I were committing a sin that cried to heaven for vengeance, I cut a slit in the lining of my overcoat and inserted the programs: so that by the end of the week I had so many programs stuffed into the lining of my coat it looked like one of Scarlett O'Hara's crinolines.

Toward the end of my stay my overcoat sounded like thunder as I moved down the street, so I was careful to take it off before I went into my uncle's house. More eccentric behavior. It was a cold winter but I wouldn't put my coat on in the house, I carried it around very gingerly and put it on when I got outside. They really must have thought I was crazy. I saw all the shows and arrived back in Braddock with all the programs and lied about the tear in the lining of my coat, lies lead to lies. The programs were pored over by me and my friends and eventually became tattered and torn from much reading. My cousins still think Manhattan is a perfidious place and my Uncle James thought till the end that the theater was a corrupt place full of Communists or worse, but I still have those programs and I'm still the theater-mad dance-nut I was when I first came to Manhattan in 1942—the only difference is that I seldom hide my programs in my overcoat.

Black Rock Dreams

Some years ago I ran a small but distinguished company called Popular Library, which was bought by CBS which made William Paley, in effect, my boss. I didn't actually run the company: I was the editor in chief. The company was run by some dim-witted Harvard MBA's who eventually ran the thing into the ground.

These Harvard MBA's used to take me to meetings at Black Rock—CBS headquarters—because I was the only one who could make Mr. Paley laugh. I loved going there. The meetings took place in Mr. Paley's private dining room and I would sit there and let the bullshit flow over my head, all the time staring at museum-quality Braques, Picassos and Modiglianis, meanwhile eating first-class food (Mr. Paley's chef was the best) after the allowed single drink. Mr. Paley had been conned into buying Popular Library for about ten times what it was worth, and he was furious and couldn't figure how it had been done. I'd been with the previous management and I knew how it had been done and he knew I knew, and I knew he knew I knew and he used to look me in the eye and say "Mr. O'Connor how did this happen?" And I used to do my Carol Channing imitation: "Why Mr. Paley sir, I have no idea, sir."

While at Popular Library I published a sensational book called *Rock Dreams*, a series of super-realist paintings of rock stars from Buddy Holly to the Rolling Stones with text by Nik Cohn. The book was bizarre, borderline obscene: The Stones were in full drag, and in one painting, Jerry Lee Lewis's thirteen-year-old wife had her finger in a place where it ought not to have been. I was sitting at one of the meetings in Mr. Paley's private dining room, gazing at the Braque, when suddenly I became aware of the angry voice of John Backe, then president of CBS. "Whose responsible for this *Rock Dreams*?" it thundered. I thought, well, there goes the job and I answered "I am." Mr. Backe was just taking a deep breath, no doubt to fire me and/or denounce me as a pornographer, when the arrival of Mr. Paley was announced. We all rose from our seats, as was the CBS custom, and when we sat

Patrick O'Connor

down, Mr. Paley asked gruffly, "Who's responsible for this *Rock Dreams*?"

I thought not only am I going to be fired, I'll probably go to jail. Mr. Paley was a powerful man who consorted with presidents. He continued, "Mr. O'Connor, do you suppose you could meet me for lunch in SoHo and we could go to the gallery and buy some of those originals for the Museum of Modern Art?" Saved by the Bill.

50

The Bad John

A few minutes ago I went down in the elevator with John Simon at 666 Fifth Ave—the sign of the devil. He was probably coming out of a Warner Brothers screening. About ten years ago in New York there used to be three John Simons, the good John Simon, the bad John Simon and the other John Simon. One was an editor, one was in the record business and the bad John Simon was and is the actor's friend, the theater critic for *New York* Magazine, the John Simon who I just saw in the elevator. He is probably the most hated man in New York though Frank Rich of *The New York Times* is giving him a run for his money. I know it's Christmas season and I should not be telling bad John Simon stories but I can't help myself. A friend of mine, Carolyn Fireside, to be precise, lived in the neighborhood of the bad John Simon, mid-thirties off Lexington Ave.

She saw him a lot in the neighborhood. She was waiting in her dry cleaning establishment one day for bad John Simon to finish his business and he was giving the man behind the counter a hard time. Now the man behind the counter was just a guy who came in from Queens every day and he didn't know John Simon from George Jean Nathan, he just knew him as a customer. After the bad John Simon left the guy behind the counter said to my friend Carolyn Fireside, "Now, that's the meanest man in New York."

Ready for one more. I used to review theater for Channel 13. In fact, I replaced John Simon. Once at a party, I said to him "You know John no matter who attacks you, and as you know many do, I always defend you because my first rule in life is that there is no such thing as a bad Serbian." He said to me in that strangest of all accents "You know, Patrick, I am half Hungarian." I said well that explains it.

I stopped reviewing for a long time but one day I ran into John at a party (I happened to be with Alan Schneider and Zelda Fichhandler of the Washington Arena Theater). John greeted me and said "Patrick, I don't see you at the theater anymore. Why don't you review anymore?" I said "No John, I finally got a grown-up job."

Suspenders

I had never thought of wearing suspenders but one day I saw a particularly beautiful pair in the window of Elizabeth Arden's, of all places. I am one of the world's great bargain shoppers and ordinarily I wouldn't think of going into a shop like Elizabeth Arden's but it was just before Christmas so I went in and bought a present for myself; they were expensive. I enjoyed wearing them and I kept my eye out for another pair but no cigar; there were no decent suspenders to be had either in New York or anywhere else in the United States for that matter.

My fortunes rose and I began to make one or two trips to Europe a year and Europe was loaded with beautiful suspenders: in London at the Burlington Arcade, where they are called braces, and in Paris at the department store Au Printemps. I bought one or

53

two pair a year so eventually I had quite a collection, though my favorite pair was given to me by my friend Leonore Fleischer. They were beautiful brown silk and subtly woven into the fabric was the word kosher written a hundred times in Hebrew.

Even then, this was in the seventies, really beautiful suspenders cost fifty bucks a piece. In New York people used to say open your coat and let me see your suspenders and I would oblige and women, especially, would "oooh and ah," and inevitably ask me to bring a pair home for their husbands or fathers. I always said sure, give me fifty bucks and I'll be delighted. They never did, though I was offered the moon for the ones that said kosher. After a few years I had quite a supply of extraordinary suspenders and people never stopped asking to see them and to bring them back a pair the next time I went to Europe.

One day in the Burlington Arcade, off Piccadilly, in my usual "braces" shop they were having a gigantic sale. Some of the most beautiful suspenders I had ever seen were going for the equivalent of five bucks. I said "Wrap them up I'll take them all," thinking that from then on every time someone asked me about suspenders I could just give them a pair. I bought a hundred pair. The wily shopkeeper allowed as how he would send a few at a time in small pack-

ages to my office in New York so I wouldn't have to
pay customs and all in all I was quite delighted with
the deal. The world's great bargain shopper strikes
again. The suspenders arrived and I stored them in a
closet in the office and forgot about them. One day at
a liquid lunch my luncheon companion said her father
would just love a pair of suspenders of the kind I was
wearing so I took them off right there at the table and
gave them to her. I was a little porky at the time (I'm
always a little porky) so I didn't have any trouble holding my trousers up. When I got back to the office I took
out one of the unopened packages of suspenders, select-
ed a pair, and tried them on. I had been had, the damn
things were for midgets which is why, I suppose, they
were so cheap. Well not for midgets exactly but for
extremely short men of which I am one. What to do,
what to do with one hundred pair of beautiful English
braces for extremely short men. I brooded about it for
a long time.

Around Christmas of that year I had an idea.
The bible of the publishing industry is a thick book
called *Literary Market Place*, known affectionately as
LMP. It's as large as a telephone book, in fact, it is the
telephone book of the publishing industry, and is used
as such. Publishing houses and their staffs are listed
up front and everyone who works in the publishing

industry is listed. I went through it with a fine tooth comb and underlined everyone I knew, and some I didn't know very well, who was under five foot five (my height), wrapped them up a Christmas present and sent them out.

I was sitting at my desk a few days before Christmas and the phone rang and it was a friend, Annette Wells, she said "O'Connor what's going on, I was sitting in Nat Sobel's office and he opened up this Christmas present from you, there was a nice card and a magnificent pair of suspenders and he cried, now I want to know what's going on here, you don't even like Nat Sobel and besides he's Jewish and why are you sending him elaborate Christmas presents." I said "I can't explain." "But he's crying," she said. I said "Well, you know how Jews are around Christmas if you give them a present they cry, besides I like Nat Sobel, just because I said all those ugly things about him doesn't mean I don't like him." "Well Patrick," she said, "this is very strange behavior on your part."

Years later I explained to my friend Annette what I had done but I swore her to secrecy. She laughed for days. And to this day when I go to a New York publishing party short men will come up to me open their suit coats and show the beautiful suspenders I gave them twenty years ago. And now they know why.

I Belong to New York

When I was growing up in Braddock, Pa., there was a very small pool of Irish names so we were all Pat or Mike, John or Robert, and the girls were called Agnes or Rosemary or Annarose, no self-respecting Irish family would call a child Seamus or Sean, not even Kevin. The girls were not called Bridie or Brigid or Mavourneen. First- and second-generation Irish didn't want their children to have the names of bogtrotters or upstairs maids. It took three generations for the Irish to start using fancy Gaelic names. So to distinguish all the Pats and Mikes, families would always refer to their own Pat and Mikes as OURPATTY or OURMIKEY as though it were one word. For reasons I've already explained elsewhere—Marlene Dietrich changed my name from Robert to Patrick—I was always known by my family as OURBOBBY and later as OURBOB.

In maturity I happen to think that the habit is not only OK, but that it's touching. It defines people better and places them in a tribe and I've taken to calling my brother OURPAUL and my sisters OURNANCY, OURMAUREEN and OURKATHLEEN, it makes me feel closer to them and it's only slightly pretentious. I did have one cousin who was called Francis de Salles—how about that for piety— he was named after his parish church. There was no reason for his mother and father, my Aunt Marcella and Uncle Matt, to call him OURFRANCISDESALLES, he was the only one in Allegheny County. He was in fact called "Brother." Of course, as I was growing up I didn't want to be anybody's Bobby, especially those Irish peasants who spawned me. I wanted to be my own person, single and independent. You will discover that with age you will use any prop to feel connected, and your parents change from Irish peasants to wise and wonderful mentors.

One day I was on a train in the club car speeding through Scotland heading toward the western isles and a big, burly Scotsman who had somehow changed into a kilt after we left Glasgow said "Where are you from, laddie?" He was the sort of man who called everyone laddie even though I was old enough to be his father and he was slightly hostile and aggressive about it. We had both taken in a few drops of malt as they say in

Scotland. I answered "I'm from New York," and then I said with equal hostility and aggressiveness "Where are you from?" and he said, his voice softening and his eyes misting "I belong to Skye." I was overwhelmed. I had never heard anyone tell where they were from in such a moving way. He meant he was born on the island of Skye but, of course, the way he said it conveyed so much more. "I belong to Skye." I can't imagine anyone saying "I belong to Newark, New Jersey." It just doesn't have the right ring to it.

When I was four I taught myself to read and when I was five I read about New York and I said "Someday, someday I'm going to New York City." I got here as soon as I could, and it's not always been wonderful. In fact it's been up and down, but at least it's been here and not Braddock, Pennsylvania. Another thing about growing old, when I was a boy in Braddock, Pa., I would have killed to get out of there or killed myself if I had had to stay but now Braddock, Pa., is covered with the veil of golden memory and seems in retrospect to have been the most wonderful place in the world to have grown up. However happily I remember Braddock, I nevertheless feel passionately about New York City and have never regretted . . . . regretted, hell I have been grateful all my life that I've had the privilege of living here, up and down or no. Next week I'm going away for a bit. Inevitably I'll meet strangers and they'll ask me where I'm from and I'm going to try it on for size. I'm going to say "I belong to New York."

Black Is Beautiful

Mei Ling Fang was the great Chinese actor of the twentieth century. So popular was he that he was the favorite of Mao Tse-tung and Chiang Kai-shek. He played women. In the thirties, Mr. Mei came to the United States for a short tour and the person who was hired as his interpreter was the distinguished scholar and curator of Oriental Art at the Metropolitan Museum, Alan Priest, who spoke perfect Mandarin. Mr. Mei gave a performance in Boston and after the performance there was a reception for *tout* Boston. There was a reception line and Mr. Priest was at Mr. Mei's elbow. One of the more formidable Boston Brahmin dowagers after she had complimented Mr. Mei on his performance said to Mr. Priest's horror: "Mr. Mei, as you probably know all Chinese look alike to us. I wonder what we look like to you." Mr. Priest was shocked at the insensitivity of the remark but said to himself what the hell let the old trout hang herself. So he translated the question literally. Mr. Mei smiled sweetly and said "On the contrary I think some of the black ones are quite beautiful."

Boy Genius

I was once editor in chief of a magazine called *Silver Screen*. My highbrow friends were ashamed of me but I had quite a good time writing those headlines "What Did Sammy Davis Jr. and Liz and Richard Do in the Dorchester Hotel." They did nothing but have a cup of tea but you would have never known it from the headlines. I knew a great deal about film but I didn't know anything about movies and movie stars. I was working as a book editor for the company that published *Silver Screen*, and the editor, Ira Peck, quit. I knew he was making a hell of a lot more money than I was as a lowly book editor so I went to the boss and asked for the job. The boss said you don't know Annette Funicello from Frankie Avalon. I said I'm smart and I'll learn. I got the job.

A friend, Jackie Egan, gave me a copy of a

magazine called *Film Fan Monthly*, published in Teaneck NJ. It was a scholarly fan magazine, if you can believe such a thing. I was fascinated and subscribed to it.

Some years later, having abandoned *Silver Screen*, I was working as an editor at New American Library and the president of N.A.L., Sidney Kramer, asked me if I could find someone to put together a book to be called *TV Movies*, in imitation of one he had done at Bantam Books called *Movies on TV*, when he was president of Bantam. He said I could have $30,000 to do the job.

I called around to various agents and packagers and they all said such an undertaking from scratch, which amounted to an encyclopedia of film, would cost $100,000. I was at my wits end to find someone to do this project for the budget I had when suddenly I thought of *Film Fan Monthly*. Surely I said to myself the editor of *Film Fan Monthly* would be the ideal person to put together a comprehensive list of movies to be shown on TV and make it better than *Movies on TV*. At this point I had been a subscriber to *Film Fan Monthly* for five years.

I couldn't seem to make a connection with the editor of *Film Fan Monthly*. He wouldn't come to New York to have lunch. No, he didn't want me to come to Teaneck. He wouldn't make an evening appointment.

I could tell he was interested but I couldn't tell why he couldn't see me. I began to have all sorts of fantasies about him. That he was ninety years old, hopelessly crippled, a drunk, an addict, an inmate in an institution. Finally he said he would come to Manhattan and meet on a Saturday. When he walked into my office on Saturday morning the first thing I said to him was "My God, you have acne." He was seventeen years old. I had been reading his magazine for five years and he was now seventeen. It meant that when I had originally subscribed to the magazine the editor in chief was twelve. He couldn't come to New York to negotiate his contract because his mother wouldn't let him.

I said "Listen kid, are you sure you can do this project." He said yes. I kept from the management of New American Library that I was dealing with a seventeen-year-old boy. I negotiated the contract with the boy but his father signed it. When I handed him the first advance check for $10,000, I said "How does it feel to have a check for $10,000?" He said "Beats bagging groceries in the supermarket."

I held my breath for six months knowing what a gigantic project it was and how inadequate the pay. Six months to the day (on time) this young man delivered the most beautiful, clean, complete manuscript it has been my pleasure to work with. When I told the publicity department that the author of our new—better than Bantam—*TV Movies* book was only seventeen they flipped. It is very easy to book a seventeen-year-old author on the "Today Show." The young man was Leonard Maltin who you see on "Entertainment Tonight" every night and who has become the world's authority on movies.

He went on to write a number of movie books for me: the first serious Preston Sturges book, the first Don Siegel book. The first book on minor character actors.

One of the things I think is extraordinary about Leonard Maltin is from the time he was in Junior high school he never wrote a story, a book report or a theme for school that he didn't get paid for by selling it to a magazine.

The *TV Movies* we started in 1969 is in more homes than the Bible. And it's still better than the competition. So a salute to boy-genius Leonard Maltin.

Lady Peel

      I remember wonderful Beatrice Lillie in a show called *Inside U S A*. She led a chorus that sang "Come, oh, come to Pittsburgh where friends are true as steel." She was truly a comic genius. I have a story about her that I think no one knows. My internist was a certain Dr. Prutting, an aristocratic New Yorker with an office on Park Ave. How I got to him is simple: His eccentricity was treating recovering alcoholics for practically nothing and in this he was a saint. When he was a young man he was covering for a colleague and he got a call from Beatrice Lillie's maid telling him that Miss Lillie otherwise known as Lady Peel was very ill and to come quickly to her apartment on East End Ave. He went, examined her and found her suffering from pneumonia. In spite of being quite a self-confident young man he was rather intimidated by Miss Lillie so

when it came time to give her a shot of penicillin in
her buttocks he said "Lady Peel, your derrière please."
As she was turning over in bed more dead than alive,
Miss Lillie managed to say "My Londonderry Air."

Miss Edith

      Miss Edith Dodson was the sister of the distinguished African-American poet, playwright, teacher Owen Dodson. Professor Dodson or "Fesser" as he was affectionately known to some was an inspiration to many generations of African-American theatrical artists and writers and he filled up the landscape wherever he went but the one person he didn't crowd was Miss Edith. The Fesser used to say about Miss Edith "that little girl is something else." Well, Miss Edith was not a "little girl," and though she was very short she was a giant, and she was, indeed "something else." She was under five feet tall, mahogany color, with protruding eyes and protruding teeth. Her eyes made her resemble a frog and she was to put it as kindly as possible homely. Miss Edith was the middle child of five. There was an older brother about whom very little is known and an older sister Lillian but when the Dodson's parents died prematurely Edith, though still a young girl, took over the raising and education of her two young brothers: Owen and Kenneth. Miss Edith worked "out," meaning she was a domestic and in those days, the early thirties, working "out" meant doing windows, floors, cooking, cleaning and taking care of children and whatever else white folks wanted you to do. Miss Edith had two jobs and she managed to send Kenneth to Lincoln University, an all-black school outside of Philadelphia, and Owen to Bates College in Maine. Both boys were bright and they did win scholarships (Owen was Phi Beta Kappa) but it was Miss Edith who saw to everything and paid for everything. After graduating from Bates, Owen won a scholarship to the Yale Drama School. After both boys were educated Miss Edith decided it was time for her to go to school and she did, night school. And after many years she got her BA from City College and after even more years of night school, an MSW. Miss Edith lived at 125th St and St. Nicholas Ave in the middle of everything, and even after she acquired her degrees and began to work days as a social worker she continued to help those as we like to say less fortunate: She taught typing in a Harlem night school and she helped young black men to prepare for the police exam. Her life was devoted to other people. Her brother Owen after graduating from Yale taught for several years at Hampton Institute and then at Howard University, where he eventually became head of the drama department.

I was visiting Owen in Washington D.C. when he received an invitation to the White House to celebrate the five-hundredth anniversary of Shakespeare's birth. He was disappointed that it was the Johnson and not the Kennedy White House but he was thrilled nevertheless. He said to me *"Child I'm going to take Miss Edith and what do you think that little girl will say." I said "There's only one thing a woman says when she's invited to an important event. She'll say 'What will I wear?'"*

Fesser got on the phone with Miss Edith in New York, I was on the extension, he told her about the invitation, and she was thrilled and touched that he had invited her to go with him and she said "What will I wear?" I said "Go to Elizabeth Arden and buy yourself a light blue linen suit, a white hat, gloves, bag and shoes this is an important event and I'm taking Owen to Lewis Thomas Saltz today and I'm going to make him buy a navy linen blazer and white linen pants and you'll both look like quality folks."

Miss Edith arrived in the District as it's called three days in advance of the big event with her linen suit in her suitcase and made an appointment with the local hairdresser to have her hair straightened. When she came back from the beauty parlor her hair was straight as a die but unfortunately the District was hot and humid and by the next morning Miss Edith's hair was as kinky as Brillo so she made another appointment. All in all she went to the hairdressers three times three days in a row and each time the Washington weather kinked it up. Finally she said "They're just going to have to accept me kinky hair and all."

On the day of the big event April twenty-third Miss Edith began ironing the linen early in the morning—both hers and Owen's—and they got dressed two hours in advance. They decided they would get dressed and then sit down and have a drink to steady their nerves though Miss Edith scarcely drank. Well of course an hour after they got dressed in their linen clothes they were as wilted as wet dishrags. They took everything off and Miss Edith ironed everything again, she was a good and experienced ironer. Finally they were ready, crisp linen and kinky hair but proud and happy and a little apprehensive; Miss Edith's only trip to the White House had been as a tourist. They went out on the street and hailed a cab, once they were settled and an effort was made not to crease the linen the Fesser said in his most stentorian voice "The White House, please."

The cab driver did a double take. They arrived, the invitation was inspected and they walked into the East Room, where they were greeted by a gracious Mrs. Johnson. The room was filled with the stars of the theater: Katherine Cornell, Helen Hays, Maurice Evans, Shakespearean scholars, people from the Folger Library and assorted critics and theatrical and academic folk. They were dazzled by the company, charmed by Mrs. Johnson though they both wished it had been Jacqueline Kennedy, and Professor Dodson of Howard University whispered into Miss Edith's ear that wonderful line of Gwendolyn Brooks's "We are the only colored people here."

Now Miss Edith had paid her dues probably more dues than anyone in that room: windows washed, floors scrubbed, the aching tiredness of twelve years of night school. Two sometimes three jobs. Teaching roomfuls of adolescent black girls to type and teaching them how not to get pregnant, coaching generations of young black men the techniques of passing civil service exams all of this at night after working all day for the city as a social worker. Though Professor Dodson felt ill at ease in the same room with one of his idols Katherine Cornell Miss Edith felt quite at home. So at home in fact that she told a young pipe-smoking professor who in spite of the linen-creasing heat was wearing tweed to get his feet off the chairs. After all the chairs in the East Room were in a very real sense her property.

Finally President Johnson made an appearance and Professor Dodson said though it seemed unlikely he seemed somewhat ill at ease among all these academicians and intellectuals so he spent an inordinately long time with a drama critic John Mason Brown who though an intellectual was a Texan. Miss Edith grew quite impatient and to her brother's horror marched right up to the President and said "Mr. President you've spent quite a lot of time with these famous people I would like your attention because I have a few things to say." Whatever else one might say about Lyndon Johnson he fancied himself a Texas gentleman, he leaned right over and it was a long way to lean, Miss Edith under five feet and the President well over six feet. Miss Edith began to talk in earnest directly to the President and he listened to this homely frog-like-looking black lady in her Elizabeth Arden blue suit as though he were hypnotized. She told him everything: the failure of the public schools, the failure of the welfare system but not just what was failing but what could be done about it. Her brother Owen was transfixed with fear sure that any minute the Secret Service or the FBI would come and arrest these "uppity niggers" (his phrase). The President asked Miss Edith to come into the Oval Office, where they could continue uninterrupted. He never spoke, only listened. Finally after an hour the two of them returned to the East Room, the President looking dazed and Miss Edith looking satisfied. And then after shaking hands with all those present Professor Dodson and Miss Edith left the White House. By now their linen clothes looked like crepe paper. In the cab Miss Edith took out a pocket mirror and looked at her hair, it was still as kinky as Brillo and she didn't mind at all.

Men Who Like Women

Ex-Prime Minister Edith Cresson of France says that Anglo-Saxon men are not interested in women and I wonder if that's true. Peter Brook, the English director before he was THE Peter Brook, directed soldier shows on troop ships during World War II and he said he always picked straight men to play women because they insisted on being pretty and proper because they liked women. Clinically homosexuals are not supposed to like women and anyone who has ever seen a drag queen in full throttle knows what I mean but I've known some astonishing passionate alliances between straight women and gay men. Well, the Freudians have been wrong about a number of things and perhaps they are wrong about that.

As an amateur sociologist, I keep my eye open for men who actually like women and one such is a

Swedish ski instructor I know named Claus, as in Santa Claus (no name changes here). He likes to be with women, he likes how they smell, with or without perfume, he likes to talk to them but more important he likes to listen to them (that's the biggie) and of course he's not a Don Juan, we all know about him. I asked Claus my ultimate "Do you like women," test question. "What about those stockings drying in the bathroom, forever and ever." Claus said: "Sometimes before I shave I take those stockings and kiss them." OK Claus.

One summer some years ago I went to the American Dance Festival at Duke University to participate in a dance critics conference. I arrived early. They had turned one of the dormitories into a hotel and the young man who had been hired to run the dormitory-cum-hotel arrived at the same time I did and he didn't know which end was up or what was happening on campus. He was a huge overdeveloped handsome football player filling in the time between graduation and the University of Chicago Law School. He was a nice guy and I helped him out a little and then went to my room. When I came downstairs about two hours later his eyes were bugging out. He said "I think I died and went to heaven, I've never seen so many beautiful women in my life." The dancers had begun to arrive by the hundreds and as I can testify from having lived

around Lincoln Center young fresh female dancers are
the most beautiful creatures in the world: Their com-
plexions from all that sweating, the straight backs, the
beautiful necks, what the Victorians used to call the
regard of a beautiful woman. As Chris said about all
of them "No tits but wow." Chris was in ecstasy and I
recognized in Chris one of those rare American men
who like women. We stood there schmoozing for a
while while a parade of the most beautiful women in
the world (no tits) walked by. I had an idea. By the way,
the young man's last name was Kringle so of course
he was called Chris (I'm not going to change the real
names of the people in this story to make it sound more
authentic). I said if for the rest of your life wherever
you are you want a sure way to meet the most beautiful women in any given area, learn to take a ballet class.
He did what you might expect a big overdeveloped
football player to do when told he should take ballet
class. I warmed to my subject. If you learn to take class,
no matter where you will be Keokuk, Moscow, Paris,
London or St. Petersburg, all you have to do is look up
in the Yellow Pages, find out where the local dance
school is and, *voilà*, the most beautiful girls in the world.

    At every modern dance festival there's always
a beginners' ballet class and I asked the lady who was
teaching it if she would take Chris. Of course she was

delighted. He took his first class in jeans and tennis shoes and then we went into Durham and bought him some dance togs.

This story does not have a happy ending, by the way. As so often happens to people, Chris got hooked on ballet class and by the middle of the summer he was taking five classes a day. He was also meeting beautiful women but after five classes a day he didn't have the energy to take his clothes off let alone get it up. He had, he said, the most wonderful summer of his life. He left Duke for the University of Chicago and we spoke on the phone from time to time. He was so busy going to dance class in Chicago that he flunked out of law school and that first Christmas he started jobbing around Aurora and Rockford and various *Nutcrackers*. Well, the truth be he wasn't very good but he was strong as an ox and he could lift any Sugar Plum Fairy in the state of Illinois. He could have lifted Roseanne Barr in the unlikely event that she had been dancing the Sugar Plum Fairy. Of course, he didn't tell his family but someone who knew his family saw him in the Kenosha *Nutcracker* and told them. When his family confronted him my name was mentioned and they consulted their lawyer to see if they didn't have a case against me. His father mentioned something about putting a contract out on me. Chris started too late but he still goes to

class every day—he's in advertising in Minneapolis—
he flies to New York to see the New York City Ballet.
He is the strongest supporter of dance in the entire state
of Minnesota and do I feel bad. No. I showed a guy
who really likes women how to meet them and I saved
the world the burden of another lawyer.

Head Skis
with Name Engraved

The "Kohler Strike" (plumbing supplies, Kohler, Wisc.) was one of the longest and bitterest strikes in the history of industrial America. When I was a young Trotskyite in the forties (you would be surprised how many Trotskyites there were in the forties) I used to attend sing-outs, concerts and parties to raise money for the Kohler strikers just as young people now attend concerts for the benefit of the rainforest, the hungry and the homeless. (The more things change the more they stay the same.)

In later years I betrayed my ideals and became one of those ordinary, run-of-the-mill, routine East Coast liberal Democrat pinkos but I still held on to some of my revolutionary fervor. I was at the opening day of Stratton Mt. and was going up on a chairlift with a stranger. I looked at his skis and all over the front of them there appeared in large letters KOHLER, Kohler, Wisc., and I said "Don't tell me those m____ f___'s are making skis." He looked at me with as much dignity and scorn as he could muster and said, "I am Mr. Kohler." Well, it was in the days when people used to have their names engraved on their Head Skis. When I went to the men's room and saw those new gleaming porcelain urinals all with the name Kohler prominently stamped on them I knew I had met Mr. Kohler himself.

Secret Weapon

During the run of the Kirov at the Met the Russians unveiled a secret weapon that no amount of weaponry research on the part of the U.S. could duplicate. In a ballet called *Potemkin*, based on the same material as the Serge Eisenstein film, thirty-five healthy young male Soviet dancers hopped around the stage for about an hour. You couldn't call it choreography, there hasn't been any choreography out of the Soviet Union since nineteen-twenty-one, but there was a lot of vigorous hopping around. Finally the sailors of the *Potemkin* overcome their decadent officers and victory is at hand.

They strip to the waist and then a spotlight shines down the left aisle of the Met and the thirty-five sweaty sailors come rushing up the aisle in triumph, hands over their heads waving like fury and yelling in

Russian. A solid wave of underarm odor hits the audience like a missile. I thought I would faint. The important ballet critic sitting next to me was so turned on he went chasing the dancers up the aisle. I must say, in fairness, that the audience loved the ballet. How the audience felt about the secret weapon I really can't say.

Frankenstein

When I was an assistant agent at MCA I had
to do the dirty work for an agent named Bobby Sanford.
We handled, that is to say, we represented an actor
named Darren McGavin, and one day the phone rang
about five P.M. and it was Darren and he was desperate. He said my wife and I are dressed to go somewhere
to receive an award and the baby-sitter hasn't arrived
and the reserve baby-sitters are all busy and none of
our relatives is answering the phone and we are really
stuck and you've got to come and baby-sit our children. They had two, one around twelve and one around
six. Darren McGavin was, in fact, a nice guy, unlike
many of our clients, and I had done many things since
I had become an agent, or really an assistant agent, but
I wasn't about to baby-sit for anyone and I told him so.
He begged and pleaded but I was adamant. My boss

as usual was in the country but I would have been just as adamant if he had been there.

But then I had a truly bizarre idea. Boris Karloff, another of our clients, lived with his wife in the same building as Darren McGavin. I knew that the Karloff's never did anything, never went out, not even to a restaurant. They were extremely nice, if tight-fisted. I called Mrs. Karloff and explained the situation and she said "Oh you mean those nice young girls I see in the elevator, we'd be delighted." The Karloffs had no children and like many adults with no children they loved them. I called Darren and told him I had found the most reliable baby-sitters in the world, someone from his own building, they would be there instantly but I didn't tell him who it was. If I told him his baby-sitters were going to be Boris and Mrs. Karloff he might have had a heart attack.

I'll let Mr. Karloff take over from here. I never called him Boris by the way, always Mr. Karloff. "We went down to the fourth floor, knocked on the door. Mr. McGavin and his wife came to the door, he in dinner clothes, she looked ravishing. Though we had been nodding in the elevator for years, I said 'Patrick said you needed a baby-sitter, I'm Boris Karloff and this is my wife.'" (Mr. Karloff did not describe the look on Darren's face. Mr. K. was not good at details but Darren's wife did and she said it was a sight to behold.) The McGavins left. Mr. Karloff continues: "We went into the sitting room, sat down but no sign of any girls. We sat for a long time and became quite alarmed wondering what happened to the children. Finally a beautiful twelve-year-old girl all in black—tutu, top, stockings, ballet shoes—pirouetted into the room, paused, went into a perfect arabesque and held it. Trying to make conversation I said 'And what do you want to be when you grow up?' The girl got up on point, did another series of pirouettes and just before she went twirling out of the room she said over her shoulder 'A widow.'"

Transitads

A few years ago I was working for Washington Square Press, a sort of highbrow division of Pocket Books. My assistant Sarah Whittier fell in love with Oscar Hijuelos's first book called *Our House in the Last World* and like all assistants in the book business, begged, pleaded and cajoled me into reading it. As a matter of fact that's a pretty good definition of what the book business is all about: begging, pleading and cajoling people to read. Most editors don't care about sales. They would gladly give the books away if only someone would read them.

I read *Our House in the Last World* by Oscar Hijuelos and like my assistant I fell in love with it. But at the time I thought if I buy one more literary novel that doesn't sell I'm going to get fired. I got fired anyway but on with the story. *Our House in the Last World* was published by a hopelessly noble hardcover company called Persea Press that in spite of publishing great books didn't have two sticks to rub together. I began to see huge ads for *Our House in the Last World* on every subway and bus in New York City—an ad campaign that surely cost hundreds of thousands of dollars. The city was blanketed with ads for Mr. Hijuelos's first novel. I was not just puzzled I was dumbfounded. Based on liking the book and perhaps just a little on the mysterious ad campaign I bought the paperback reprint rights for Washington Square Press for the price of a publishing lunch. Calvin Trillin says an author should never accept as an advance less than the cost of the lunch. Well that was about the size of the advance. His distinguished hardcover publisher called me up and said Mr. Hijuelos would like to have lunch with you. One of the reasons to be in the paperback business is you never have to have lunch with writers but I was so in love with Mr. Hijuelos's book I made an exception. We had quite a nice lunch, we talked about music, he's a musician. We talked about growing up Cuban in New York, he's Cuban. We talked about a lot of things but we never talked about what Mr. Hijuelos did for a living. By now he had made a fast two thousand bucks from his book. I think it's rude to ask someone what they do for a living but I always manage somehow, so at the end of the lunch I said "Mr. Hijuelos what do you do to buy groceries?" and he said "I work for Transitads."

Frick

      I went to the Frick Collection to see a show of
watercolors by François-Marius Granet, the nineteenth-
century French painter. Granet is famous for the portrait Ingres did of him in 1807. It is said to be the most
famous portrait in French art of the nineteenth century.
You would know it if you saw it. It's a likeness of a
handsome young man but after you study it for a while
you realize that the handsome young man has goofy
eyes and that he looks like a stand-up comic about to
get off a zinger. Not Jerry Lewis but not not Jerry Lewis.
Goofy eyes or not, M. Granet was a wonderful water-
colorist and it's worth a trip to the Frick basement. The
Frick is one of the three best places to look at art in the
United States, the other two being the Phillips Gallery
in Washington, D.C. and the Kimball in Fort Worth,
Texas. Not the greatest collections in the world, but the

rightist: in size, scope, everything. Charles Tauss, the person I know who knows most about art says the real treasure of New York City is Van Eyck's "Portrait of the Virgin, Saints and Donor" and if the city were burning that's the one painting he would try to save. I don't agree but I see what he means.

My problem with the Frick is special: The building and the collection were built out of the blood of my grandfather, and my great uncles and every time I enter that building I get a chill and I feel like a traitor. To compound my feelings of guilt, the curator of the Frick and the author of the catalog of the François-Marius Granet show is Edgar Munhall. Munhall is the name of the town in which those poor benighted steelworkers lived who were shot and killed at the time of the Homestead strike, under orders from Henry Clay Frick.

So here's my revenge, such as it is. There is a magnificent stairway in the Frick leading to the second floor and in a little alcove on the first landing of the stairway, there is a pipe organ and on the wall a wonderful Christmas-cardy Renoir. A friend and I play a little game. He pretends that he's Frick sitting in that little alcove with the Renoir, reading the *Herald Tribune*, and I pretend I'm Mrs. Frick standing at the head of the stairs in curlers and a tacky bathrobe. And I yell in a thick Yiddish accent, "Frick, Frick come to bed, Frick."

Jed Harris

I was sitting at my desk one afternoon trying to remember the words to "Margie," when the phone rang and a voice at the other end said "This is Jed Harris," there was a long pause and then he said "I'm not dead." I was transfixed. When I was growing up Jed Harris was the King of Broadway, in fact, it was said that he invented the modern New York theater with his production of the play *Broadway*.

He also produced an endless list of distinguished hits, among others: *Our Town*, and *The Front Page*. After I got over my initial shock I said "Mr. Harris, I know you're not dead, the first thing an Irishman does in the morning is read the obituaries which is why they are called the Irish funnies." Mr. Harris said, "Someone told me you know a lot about dance and you're no bullshitter. I want you to meet me at the Algonquin Hotel at six for drinks."

I walked to the Algonquin from Fortieth and Lex hoping against hope that I would meet someone over fifty who would say "Where are you going?" so I could say "I'm going to the Algonquin to have drinks with Jed Harris."

We met, and he immediately began firing questions at me about American dance and it was obvious within minutes that the man was a genius: His questions were searching and perceptive. He had a wonderful idea for a Broadway show about the history of American dance though he knew very little about it. After he got all the information he needed from me he turned on his charm, which was considerable.

If you've ever taken a course in playwriting the instructor always uses *The Front Page*, by Ben Hecht and Charles MacArthur, directed by George S. Kaufman, as an example of the great American farce and the curtain line of *The Front Page*, "That son-of-a-bitch stole my watch," as an example of the great American curtain line. Now there has never been any doubt about who wrote the play but there has always been some doubt about who wrote the curtain line, and some have credited it to Jed Harris himself.

After a decent interval I said "Mr. Harris, who wrote the curtain line for *The Front Page*?"

He said, at some length, "Well, you know I was having all kinds of trouble with Ben and Charlie, they wouldn't settle down, they had "spilkes in tuchas" (needles in the ass) they were drinking and fooling around and I couldn't get them to concentrate and besides Charlie was in love with that broad, what's her name?"

"Helen Hayes," I said.

"Yeah, that's right, Helen Hayes."

"It was George S. Kaufman."

Martha

There was a eulogy for Martha Graham in today's *Times* by her friend Agnes De Mille so no need for another one but here's a story about her that no one knows: Jed Harris, the man who invented Broadway and one of the great producers/directors of all time, was about to produce *A Doll's House* with Ruth Gordon and the script calls for Nora to do a tarantella. He called up his friend John Murray Anderson and said, "Whose the best dancer in New York?" and John Murray Anderson said "Martha Graham." Jed Harris said "Never heard of her, but give me her number." This was before anyone had heard of Martha Graham. He called Martha Graham and told her that he wanted her to teach Ruth Gordon the tarantella and she agreed. These are now mostly Jed Harris's words: Martha Graham arrived at the theater in the most beautiful coat I had ever seen which she had clearly made herself, she wore a hat, gloves and she carried what was unusual for the time a bag which was a cross between the briefcase of a businessman and a doctor's bag (her father was a Dr.). She looked in fact like a woman Dr. making a house call. I took her on stage, introduced her to Miss Gordon and I retired to the back of the house where I could watch. Miss Graham took off her coat, left her extraordinarily stunning hat on, put her bag down and proceeded to teach Ruth Gordon the tarantella in a record twenty minutes, I had never seen anything like it. Martha Graham put on her beautiful coat, shook hands with Miss Gordon, came down the aisle shook hands with me and presented me with a bill which I thought was very efficient of her. The bill looked like a doctor bill. Jed Harris said later "It was all in all one of the most satisfying efficient artistic and business exchanges I had ever experienced."

One I Go To, One I Wouldn't Set Foot In

I used to get three copies of every dance book published which requires some explanation. I was a paperback book publisher so a copy was sent to me by the hardcover publisher to try and sell me the paperback rights; I was an easy target since I was the only paperback publisher who published dance books; I was also a dance critic so I was sent a copy in the hopes that I would review it; the third copy is a little trickier to explain. Since I knew everyone who wrote dance books and the writers couldn't get agents, no money in it, I would go over their contracts for them gratis to see that they weren't being cheated (they never were). As a result the writers would send me an autograph copy. Dance books began to pile up in my office, in my home and in the homes of my friends plus I had my own considerable collection.

I called Arthur Mitchell, founder and head of the Dance Theater of Harlem and since the death of Dorothy Day the only genuine saint in Manhattan. I said Arthur who runs your library and Arthur said we don't have a library. I said Arthur you have to get off your black asses and start a library because you can't have a school without a library. Arthur said "Yassuh, massah." Arthur calls me "massah."

I'm terribly neurotic and so instead of making a nice selection of books to send up to Harlem for its new library I started pulling everything including, alas, those wonderful Barbara Morgan photos of Martha Graham from the thirties. I called Arthur and said send a truck, and they did and they ended up with a basic dance library. This story is not about generosity it's about chutzpah. A few weeks later I saw Arthur Mitchell on the street in front of Carnegie Hall; he threw his arms around me and burst into tears. He said "Patrick that's the most imaginative gift of kindness we've ever received, now when I'm teaching "Afternoon of a Faun," I can tell the kids to go to the library and look at the pictures in the books of me and Tanny from the fifties and you can see what we looked like." And then he said, "Patrick can you get us some shelves?" I said "If I get you shelves you black m____ f___ you can name it after me."

A few years later I was in Israel visiting friends
in Israeli dance and the Bath Sheva Company was doing
"The Shakers," a work by Doris Humphries in honor
of our (U.S.) Bicentennial. "The Shakers" is a dance
from the thirties about that religious group who made
such wonderful furniture but in a dance context it's
about a group of religious celibates who dance their
sexual energy away which gives a new meaning to "I'm
gonna dance off both my shoes." I said to my friend
the Baroness Rothschild (sorry) how are you ever going
to explain celibacy to the Israelis, it's not a concept
they will readily understand. The Baroness said to me,
"Mr. O'Connor have you ever heard the story about
the Rabbi and the old lady with a five-year headache?"
And I said "No." The Baroness proceeded: An old lady
has a headache for many years so she goes to her Rabbi
and complains and the Rabbi says tell me about your
headache. After the old lady talks for four hours she
says "Rabbi, Rabbi my headache is gone." And the
rabbi says "Now I have your headache."

So the Baroness says "Mr. O'Connor now it's
your headache; you have to explain celibacy to the
Israelis." I said I would and said that the next day I
would go to the dance library and find out who did the
original music and the sets etc. and that I would do a
press kit for her. The Baroness said, "What library?"

I said the dance library and she said "We don't have a dance library." I said "Israel isn't even a country (it's a book club) and you don't even have a dance library?" "No," she said emphatically.

When I got back to New York the second of my three dance books had to go to Israel. Every time a dance book was published in New York I would call up the publisher, who I usually knew and say I need three copies of the book one for Harlem, one for Israel and one for myself—the words I used were ugly racial epithets not allowed in print but you can imagine—and then I said if you don't send them to me I will put you down in my golden book of anti-Semites which I publish every year for Rosh Hashanah. You have no idea how easy it is for a goy (me) to blackmail a Jew into doing something, especially when it's for Israel. Come to think of it I guess if you know anything about our national policy you know that. So I sent thousands of books to Israel over the years giving them a basic dance library and a few years later I got a letter from the Israeli government saying that there was now a collection in Israel called the O'Connor Dance Library. Quite nice, I thought, the Irish Zionist strikes again.

There's a wonderful old Yiddish story about an old Jewish man who has been lost on a desert island for twenty years and when he's found he's in perfect health and quite happy but there's only one peculiar thing about his life on the island. Someone says to him "You've done wonderfully, you're fit and healthy you obviously flourished here but tell me why have you built two synagogues, wouldn't one have been enough?" The old man says "One I go to and one I wouldn't set foot in." Anyone who knows anything about Israel or American Jewry for that matter will not be surprised to learn that a group of rich and not-so-rich American Ladies from Central Park West started another Dance Library in Israel giving those interested one they could use; one they needn't set their feet in. So these ladies hustled me for years to combine with them and finally I gave in and now it's called the Dance Library of Israel and it's in Bat Arieal and it's the second largest dance library in the world—the New York Public is first.

I'm afraid there's a postscript: Whenever there's a party for a dance book (rare event) I always manage to hustle two copies of the book in advance so I'm not accused of stealing. I get the author to inscribe one for the Dance Theater of Harlem and one for the Dance Library of Israel—dated, signed etc. I was at a party some time ago for a book about Ruth St. Denis called *Miss Ruth*, by a nice lady named Suzanne Shelton, and I asked her to inscribe her book and she said she knew all about the libraries I was supplying with books and what a good thing etc. etc. and she said she had just returned from China, where they were desperate for dance books and I said enough: two countries, Harlem and Israel, are enough for me, I'm not taking on another one. But she slipped the address into my pocket and sure enough a few weeks later I had four copies of one book so I sent it to the address in Beijing. Well, you know that the Chinese are just like the Russians: if you give them something, however slight, they must give you something in return so after I sent a few books to a dance library in Beijing I got a big box of books from China, in Chinese, about the ballet which I immediately sent to Israel, knowing that some Israeli ballet nut could read Chinese. Please don't send me the names of any countries who need dance libraries.

Same Old
Jewish Music Freddie

Fred F. Finklehoffe was from Springfield, Massachusetts. His father was a Russian Jewish immigrant who spoke no English. It was obviously no handicap since he managed to get Fred into the Virginia Military Institute in the nineteen thirties. At the time not only did V.M.I., as the Virginia Military Institute is affectionately known, have no Jews it had no Catholics. We're talking about the Old South. In spite of being short, Jewish and unathletic, Fred managed to get through four years of V.M.I. in tact, and for his senior thesis he wrote a play called *Brother Rat*. The rest is theatrical history. The play was picked up by George Abbott, produced and directed by him and was an instant hit on Broadway and went on to be a movie starring that actor who later played our president. So here was twenty-one-year-old short, Jewish and unathletic Fred Finklehoffe wandering around New York with a hit on his hands and probably one thousand five hundred, pre-World War II untaxable dollars in his pocket. He used to hang out at the Gotham Book Mart, where he met another young man named Charlie Gaynor. They became friends. In the spring of that year Fred's friend Charlie disappeared and Fred asked the nice folks at the Gotham Book Mart "Where's Charlie?" and they informed him that every spring Charlie went to Pittsburgh to write a musical for his college room-mate, Fred Burleigh, then, and for many years the director of the Pittsburgh Playhouse. So Fred got on a train and went to Pittsburgh for the opening of his friend's musical. By the way, a compilation of the Pittsburgh spring musicals eventually became the smash Broadway revue *Lend an Ear* and starred, for her first time on Broadway, Carol Channing.

There was Fred at the opening of Charlie's musical. The musical wasn't bad but it had in it the most spectacular singer/dancer Fred had ever seen. Of course, Fred hadn't seen much he was only twenty-one. So was the singer/dancer. Fred went backstage to talk to the young man and told him how much he liked his performance and that he should come to New York and if he did he would become a star. Well, the young man was very hesitant and said that he and his sister and brother had quite a profitable dancing school and he was doing very well and he had the musical at the Pittsburgh Playhouse to do every year and he really didn't want to go to New York. But Fred convinced him. Told him that if he came to New York they could be roommates etc. Of course you guessed that the man was Gene Kelly. When Kelly did come to New York he tried out for the chorus of *Pal Joey* and got the lead.

Eventually Fred got hired by M.G.M. to go out to Hollywood to write movies. He did what everyone did at the time: He took the *Twentieth Century* to Pasadena but there was no one there to meet him when he got off the train. When he arrived at the M.G.M. lot no one had ever heard of him, there was no office for him and no one wanted to have anything to do with him. This was a typical reaction to newly arrived writers as we know from the memoirs of the period. So having nothing to do, meanwhile collecting a large salary—he had been hired by the New York office and that's where the money came from—he hung out in the commissary. Years later I went to the M.G.M. commissary to see if they had matzohs on the table of the executive dining room and as recently as 1980 they did. Hanging out in the commissary he talked to anyone who would talk to him.

One day he was sitting at a table alone brooding when Jerome Kern walked in. Now Jerome Kern at the time was king of not just Broadway but the world, he was writing hit after hit both in New York and Hollywood. Jerome Kern knew who Freddie Finklehoffe was—the boy wonder of Broadway—and went up to his table and said "Do you mind if I sit with you Freddie?" Freddie who was dying for company said "No, Mr. Kern."

As Freddie tells the story he said "I didn't know what to say to this giant, so I asked him what he was working on." He told me he was working on a musical called Messrs Marco Polo by Donn Byrnn. "Mr. Kern you're writing a musical about an Italian? "Yes," said Mr. Kern "Who goes to China?" "Yes" said Mr. Kern again. "From a novel by an Irishman?" "Yes, again," said Mr. Kern as he continued to eat his soup. When Freddie told the story he used to say at this point "Now I really sounded like an ass I said 'Mr Kern, what kind of music are you going to write for such a show?'"

And Mr. Kern said "Same old Jewish music, Freddie."

A few years later Freddie was working for the Arthur Freed unit of M.G.M. That unit produced those glorious musicals among which were *Meet Me in St. Louis*. Freddie had written a screenplay for a musical and Mr. Freed thought it might be a good idea if Freddie pitched it to Louis B. Mayer. So an appointment was made with the ogre and Freddie and Mr. Freed went into Mr. Mayer's office. Most people when they do Louis B. Mayer do him with a Yiddish accent but in fact he didn't have one. They confuse him with all those others who did.

Freddie pitched his story which was about a tap dancer and his girl during World War I. Mr. Mayer liked the story but said "Where are we going to get a non-fegele tap dancer to play the lead?" Freddie said "As it happens your son-in-law David O. Selznick has just signed up a non-fegele tap dancer named Gene Kelly." Fegele means bird in Yiddish and it is also Yiddish for "faggot" or more appropriate for the times "fairy" and, yes, Mr. Mayer was using it pejoratively.

Mr. Mayer called his son-in-law and said "David I understand you have a non-fegele tap dancer under contract." And Mr. Selznick said "It's gonna cost you."

The movie was *For Me and My Gal* and it launched Gene Kelly's career.

Same old Irish music Freddie.

A Gentleman's Profession

Early in my publishing life I got some short stories and I think some poems from a steelworker in Turtle Creek, near my hometown, Braddock, Pa. I'm not sure why Mr. Carmine Cartazzo, for that was the gentleman's name, sent me his work but probably a story about me appeared in *The Braddock Free Press* and said that I was a New York editor. I read everything submitted to me from Pittsburgh and I devour anything from the Monongahela Valley so I'm sure I must have scribbled some encouraging words on Mr. Cartazzo's manuscript and sent it back to him. Over the years Mr. Cartazzo continued to send me bits and pieces of things he had written. I would offer suggestions as to how they could be improved and send them back. We never talked on the phone nor did we meet. It was, all in all, a very satisfactory relationship. In

109

nineteen-eighty I became editor in chief of Pinnacle Books and Mr. Cartazzo sent me a novel. It wasn't the greatest novel in the world but, what the hell, it was by an honest-to-God-steelworker from my hometown who hadn't been to college or taken a creative writing course and everyone deserves one good break. Not a big deal.

I intended to publish it as a paperback original and Mr. Cartazzo stood to make a few thousand bucks, fifteen hundred to be precise. I gave it to a very good copy editor and told her to fix it up, put Al Pacino's picture on the cover, well as close to Al Pacino as the law would allow, and gave it some outrageously romantic title, *Nowhere to Go but Home*, and started it on its way.

You may not know this but paperback books are not printed until the salesmen are through selling them. That is to say salesmen take the covers out to the bookstores and book wholesalers, get orders, call the orders in and then the book is printed based on the number of orders. It's not a foolproof system but it's better than scheduling print orders blind.

One day Stanley Reisner, the president of Pinnacle Books, came into my office and said "You know this book about the steelworker, well I have no orders for this book, none, zero, zippo so I'm not going to publish it, so call the author up and tell him we ain't publishing his book." I said "Wait a minute, where is it written in my contract that I have to call up authors and tell them that the publication of their book's been cancelled." Mr. Reisner said "Well someone has to do it and it's not going to be me so I guess it has to be you."

I put off calling Mr. Cartazzo for a few days, as a matter of fact, I was thinking of quitting so I wouldn't have to perform this onerous task. A few days later Mr. Cartazzo was on the phone about something to do with his book and I said "Mr. Cartazzo they've cancelled the publication of your book." He said "What?" I repeated "They've cancelled the publication of your book." Mr. Cartazzo said "No they ain't, nobody's cancelling the publication of my book. I told everyone, I told the guys in the mill, I told the guys on the street, I told the guys in the bar, I told the priest, I don't even go to church and I told the priest and my family. Are you guys trying to make a bullshitter out of me? You got another thing coming. You ain't cancelling my book. What's the name of the guy who signed the contract, you know, the president of the company?" I said "His name is Stanley Reisner." Mr. Cartazzo said "You tell Mr. Reisner I'm coming to New York on Friday and I'm going to kill him." And then Mr. Cartazzo said one other thing which if I were a better poet I could remember. He assured me that though he was Italian he was acting on his own, that he was not acting in concert with anyone, especially his family, that this was going to be a one on one. It was a lovely phrase, I've now heard it twice and I wish I could remember it.

I immediately went down to Stanley's office and said "Mr. Cartazzo is coming to New York on Friday and he's going to kill you." Stanley's reaction was the reaction of every middle-class Jew to every crisis. He said "I think I'll go to Miami."

I went back to my office, got on the phone to call in my western Pennsylvania markers. The truth is I have no Pa. markers. I left there when I was seventeen to go to the war and I never went back. Nevertheless, I called every department store, every book wholesaler, every book shop in Pittsburgh trying to sell them Mr. Cartazzo's book. I kept saying over and over come on I don't care whether you sell the book or not just order it if it doesn't sell you can return it for full credit. Finally after two days I had thirty thousand orders, in those days we lost more than thirty thousand copies. But I thought thirty thousand might be enough to change the boss's mind. So I took my thirty thousand orders down to his office and he said "OK, we'll print this book but I never want to hear another word about this book again."

What happens, to fill you in, before the book is published is that there are lots of upfront costs, copy-editing, typesetting, cover costs and if you can stop a book that looks like it's going to be a sure loser you can save the company twenty-five thousand dollars in plant costs by not going through with the final printing. It doesn't happen often but it happens.

The next Friday I came back from lunch and there standing in my secretary's office was, I knew, the man himself, Mr. Cartazzo. I'm short but he was shorter than me and built like a bull with hands the size of ham hocks, as wide as he was long and not an ounce of fat on him. I quickly said "We're publishing the book." He said "I know your secretary told me." He gave me a big embrace. One of those Italian bear hugs, and I could feel the gun.

We went into my office and sat down. Meanwhile galleys of the book had been sent out for review weeks prior to this and that day a good review of the book appeared in *Publishers Weekly* and I had that good news for Mr. Cartazzo. He went back to Pennsylvania without shooting anyone.

The book was published to good reviews. Mr. Cartazzo had his fifteen minutes of fame, a feature story above the center fold in the *Pittsburgh Post Gazette* and a few minutes on Pittsburgh TV. A couple of months later he called me and said "Hey, Mr. O'Connor my book is not in the stores." And I was able to say "Mr. Cartazzo you've had my best shot, that's all there is, there isn't anymore. You had better buy up whatever copies you can find you'll need them for your grand-children. And good luck on your next book."

Bovary

During World War II A-12 was the Army's plan and V-12 was the Navy's to give young bright Americans a little education before sending them off to the Battle of the Bulge or to Iwo Jima. I was a junior in high school and watched my friends in the senior class enlist and be sent off to Harvard, Yale, Princeton, and Georgetown, Georgetown, by the way, was not the hot school it later became, it was just a school for rich Catholics. Since I was as bright as most of my friends I assumed that the day after I enlisted I would be sitting under a tree in Harvard Yard.

Because of the war we were allowed to leave high school in the middle of our senior year and since I wasn't old enough to enlist I spent a semester at the University of Pittsburgh. Eager to get on with life at a better school, I enlisted on my eighteenth birthday (patriotism might have had something to do with it but it's hard, these days, to convince people of that). So a few weeks after my birthday I found myself taking infantry basic training in Camp Blanding, Florida, and living in a small hut with ten brutal, provincial, murderous red-necks, most of whom could barely read and write. They were so backward they never left the camp because they were afraid of the big city—Jacksonville. They stayed on the post drinking 3.2 beer and having knife fights on Saturday night.

For someone who had spent his life in a library and never left it except to go to the ballet it was quite a challenge. Brightness saved me and I managed to somehow get along with these hillbillies. I learned to shoot a rifle, crawl under barbed wire with machine gun bullets passing overhead, march twelve miles with a heavy pack and a rifle that was almost as tall and heavy as I was.

There's a fine line between being a smart-ass and being smart and I managed to walk it. There were classes and I knew better than to shine too much. I noticed the company commander eyeing me with suspicion. One day he said "Son, did you graduate from high school?" I refrained from saying yes and at the top of my class, I said "Yes, and I had a semester in college." He looked puzzled and walked away. He kept looking at me in this curious way and I was becoming paranoid. It doesn't do to have your company commander looking at you suspiciously. One day I was called into the office by the first sergeant. He was a red-neck but he could read and write. He said "The Captain wants you to take the IQ test again. According to our records you're a borderline retard." So that's why no Harvard, Yale, Princeton. One Saturday I and one of the sergeants who was trying to raise his IQ score up to 110 so he could go to O.C.S. went to headquarters and took the test again. The results came in and the first sergeant called me into his office and said "You're a piece of work, first you're a retard and then you're off the charts, you're outta here." (I had lots of problems but brightness was not one of them.)

Within days I was moved to an I & R unit (Intelligence and Reconnaissance), and into a hut with ten New York Jews. My longest and most steadfast love affair has been with that tribe which Djuna Barnes calls beloved of God, despised by the people. I & R men are used as scouts and in extreme cases JASCO (Joint Air Sea Command), they swim ashore with radio equipment before D-day. So I wasn't sure my new IQ score "off the charts," according to my old company commander, had served me so well.

As soon as the training was over I was sent as

an infantry man to the South Pacific, where I joined the Forty-first Infantry Division. They were known as Fuller's Butchers: Fuller was our General, and butchery describes his men's behavior in combat. They gave a new meaning to "Don't Take Prisoners."

In the beginning you are convinced that the army is such a vastly complex organization that only God could run it, and after you've been in it for a while you realize that not only is it not run by divine providence, but nobody runs it.

On my first D-day I did what any self respecting, sensitive, imaginative eighteen-year-old would do: I shit in my pants. It may not have been exactly my fault. There was a very curious D-day custom. For days before D-day we steamed through the South Pacific on our way to whatever beach we were landing on and we ate canned C rations which by the way were the precursor of the worst "health food." In other words highly concentrated, potent, tasteless, healthy stuff, good for keeping you alive but not particularly soothing for the insides. On D-day morning, that is to say at zero hour minus two or three, they served steak and prune whip, yes prune whip. I always thought it was some Australian cook's idea of a joke. Lots of jokes about fattening up for the kill. After four or five days of primitive health food and then steak and prune whip and the thought of imminent death—lucky it was only my pants I soiled. I was reading the Armed Forces edition of *H.M. Pulham Esq.* and luxuriating in using the pages I had read as toilet paper. I also had a copy of *Madame Bovery* in my pack and the reason I wasn't reading it: I didn't intend to use it as toilet paper.

As I said, during my first D-day I thought it surely had to be organized by God but by the second I knew it was not organized by anyone and once we hit the beach (at zero hour) everything remained utter chaos for forty-eight hours. It's not that bombs didn't fall, they did, and we were strafed (strafing is the worst, by the way), and that people were being killed (they were), it's that no one, absolutely no one, knew what was going on.

The battle for Zamboanga, (where the monkeys have no tails) Philippine Island was far from the bloodiest battle the Forty-first Infantry Division fought but it was exciting enough for me. There were the usual five days on the open water on an L.C.I. (Landing Craft Infantry). You've seen one of them in the movies, it's the one John Wayne gets off with his bayonet fixed to the end of his rifle. You do not get off charging but you do hold your piece (Army talk for rifle) up in the air so it doesn't get wet. Before that zero minus two or three hours, the Air Force has bombed the beach to smithereens, exciting and not unlike Macy's fireworks. It's the only time the Infantry likes the Air Force, otherwise we tell stories about their dumping mail in the Pacific so they will have room to bring booze from Australia. So at Zamboanga the Air Force pulverized the beach and we casually walked off the L.C.I.'s and confusion reigned.

Meanwhile it was impossible to dig a foxhole in the coral, though several frightened rookies tried. No matter how scared you are coral doesn't give even with a pickax: I had found that out earlier.

I had found myself a little indentation in the ground and that's where my friend Sgt. Kerr found me. He was not my sergeant but my friend the sergeant who read Yeats and Pound. He reported finding me lounging on a GI blanket looking as much like Madame Récamier as a dirty infantryman could eating C-ration chocolates, and reading.

Sgt. Kerr was an aristocrat who never ever swore but he said: "Private O'Connor what the fuck are you doing?"

"I'm weeping for Emma," I said.

"The fucking world has gone crazy and this fuck is reading fucking French novels."

Beware of
Provincial Bohemia

During the spring that I first went to the University of Pittsburgh, I tried out for a play at the Pittsburgh Playhouse and met and plunged into Pittsburgh bohemia. Chekhov tells us to beware of provincial bohemia and with good reason.

Pittsburgh bohemia like provincial bohemia everywhere is an amalgam of people from local community theater, the radicals from the local universities—in the case of Pittsburgh, the art and drama students from Carnegie Tech—and above all the department store people in what is called "display," as in window display. Someday, someone should do something about "display" people. You can be sure that the people on the cutting edge of everything in every town in the United States are "display" people. In case you've never thought of this before here's a list of display people: Andy Warhol,

Jasper Johns and Robert Rauschenberg and there are some who would say that Robert Wilson is only that.

The leader of Pittsburgh bohemia at the time was a man named Jay Looney who worked in display at Gimbels. He lived in an apartment called "The Frigging Door" on Craig St. between Forbes and Fifth Ave. in Oakland. The floors were polished, the wine bottles had wax dripping over the sides, the record player played Edith Piaf records endlessly, we read Carson McCullers *Reflections in a Golden Eye*, played charades which at that time was called "The Game," and we all considered ourselves wicked and the last word.

The Carnegie Biennial was the biggest thing in Pittsburgh: Matisse, Picasso, Kuniyoshi. It was held on the second floor of the Carnegie Museum. And our crowd said things like "Not worth the trip upstairs." I blush to think.

Always on the fringes of bohemia are the rich, why it is hard to say. And we had a number of those aristocratic hangers-on. One of them I'll call Katie Laughlin, that's not her name but her real name was equally distinguished. Though she had a house in Shadyside she allowed as how she was terribly poor. So poor was she that she devised a scheme to sell burglar alarms to her rich relatives. In addition she said if she was invited to three dinners and two luncheons a week and perhaps a wedding or funeral she really wouldn't have to buy food.

Now I was from Braddock and this was heady stuff for me. Up to that point I had hardly been in the house of a Protestant let alone an aristocrat with a name redolent of power and wealth. Finally I was invited to poor Katie Laughlin's house, "You must come to my little house one day but I can only afford to give you the skimpiest tea."

I was greeted at the door by a severe, balding man in a black jacket, and later to my horror and astonishment he served a proper English tea which consisted of any number of things I had never encountered before: cucumber sandwiches, watercress sandwiches, scones, walnut cake. I had never been served anything by anyone but my mother and grandmother. I had read enough plays and mysteries to know that the man was a butler and while he was out of the room I said "But Mrs. Laughlin if you're so poor why don't you fire your butler?" And Katie said "But, dear boy, who would answer the door?"

Yes, they are different.

Boudin

I'm deeply ashamed to admit it but my favorite painter is the French artist Eugène Boudin. He paints those little postcard-size paintings, sometimes watercolors, of La Belle Epoque ladies sitting on the beach. I know he's not a major painter but he delights me more than any other painter I know in a way that my grandmother delighted me more than any other woman I knew. I could never figure out why this particular minor painter did this to me. There was a show of Boudin in Washington at the East Wing of the National Gallery and I happened to be in Washington and I happened on the show.

There are at least two of his larger paintings and they are quite nice but you think as you look at them, well he's not Turner. But the small ones—just a strip of beach, ladies in those voluminous skirts and occasionally one of those umbrella tents on a platform with wheels and a horse or two. The ladies are mostly sitting. In one or two of the paintings the ladies look like they've just changed into bathing costumes which are just as voluminous as their street dresses. The paintings seem simple but if you examine the composition they seem monumental if the word monumental can be applied to something no bigger than a postcard. He captures perfectly the colors of the sea coast of northern France. As I stood there wondering why the paintings gave me such joy I noticed that the donors in almost every case were Mellons. Either Mr. & Mrs. Paul Mellon or a lady to whom I shall be eternally grateful called Ailsa Mellon Bruce who gave the bulk of them. It was then that I got it.

When my grandmother Rose Murphy came from Ireland at the turn of the century, though she was fourteen and alone, she managed somehow to get to Pittsburgh, where she immediately went to work as a tweenie (between upstairs maid and parlor maid) for the Mellons or the Scaifes—in Pittsburgh Mellons and Scaifes amount to the same thing. So it's really my grandmother Rose Murphy whom I dearly loved I'm seeing on the beach in the Boudin paintings. My grandmother never went to the beach but she did wear those huge voluminous Edwardian skirts which are pretty much the same as La Belle Epoque skirts the ladies in the Boudins are wearing.

Once while down on my luck in New York I worked at the most expensive men's store in the world called Knize. No job for a Trotskyite. Right? Never mind. One day a lady came in and bought a lot of frippery for a man she said was dying. And I thought poor woman, spending all her money on a dying man. She then gave me her name, Mrs. Paul Mellon. I was so busy thinking how pleased my grandmother would have been with the idea of my waiting on a Mrs. Mellon that I forgot to get her address. When I told this to my boss he said "Never mind, Mrs. Paul Mellon, Virginia, will do."

Disco

A visiting scholar from Beijing arrived in New York in July and wanted to see me and spend some time with me. I consider him a friend, though we had never met, we've been writing back and forth for six years. I was at the beach, Fire Island Pines, and he called me from Manhattan. The temperature in New York was 110 in the shade and I was not about to come into the city in all that heat so I told him if he wanted to see me he would have to come to the beach. He welcomed the idea.

I was slightly nervous about what a Chinese who had never been away from mainland China before would think of Fire Island Pines, a unique community, to say the least. One might stretch the rules of grammar and say that Fire Island Pines and Cherry Grove are two of the uniquest communities in the world.

He arrived, I greeted him on the dock, fortunately the other male-to-male greetings on the dock were unusually uneffusive. That evening we took a walk and walked past the disco. He heard the music, he wanted to go in. I did not want to go in and have to explain a gay disco to a visiting Chinese dignitary. On the other hand he is China's leading dance critic. What the hell, in we go. He sees all those magnificent overdeveloped male bodies (whatever happened to willowy sissies) in white tank tops, white shorts, those bulky wool socks and expensive sneakers. He turns to me with astonishment. "Mr. Patrick, Mr. Patrick, I don't understand (he thinks my family name is Patrick since it appears first). This is the United States—where are the wives?" Before I have a chance to mumble something inane or make up a lie, his eyes light up and he says "I know. They are home making dinner." "Right" I said.

Evelyn Waugh

I have a friend, a truly distinguished editor named Dudley Frasier who when this story took place was the publicity director of Little, Brown. Evelyn Waugh came to the United States for the first time to, as the British say, flog his book *Helena*, a book about the mother of Constantine (the nerve). Mr. Frasier was in charge of looking after Mr. Waugh. There were luncheons, parties, interviews, radio, press. Mr. Waugh was as difficult as expected, in fact he was impossibly wicked and after a week of looking after him and taking his insults Mr. Frasier retired to his apartment to get some well-deserved rest. Very early Sunday morning Mr. Waugh called and said, "Well, I've been to early mass and I suppose you've been to wherever your sort goes. I've taken the liberty of inviting Mrs. Roosevelt to the little party on Monday." Little, Brown was giving Mr. Waugh a rather grand party on the following day. Mr. Waugh went on "I hope that will be all right." Mr. Frasier was delighted at the thought of Mrs. Roosevelt, the former first lady coming to a book party and said so. Mr. Waugh said "I don't mean Mrs. Roosevelt, the journalist, I mean Mrs. Kermit Roosevelt of the Long Island Roosevelts."

One more Evelyn Waugh quote. He said "The Irish are a joyless and melancholy race who have broken the hearts of all who have tried to save them."

The Little Bird
(A New York Cab
Driver's Monologue)

"I grew up on the Lower East Side, we were so poor, you shouldn't know from it. My mother wanted me to take up the violin but we couldn't afford a violin so she made me go to dancing school, two bits a week, leotards, you know tights, tap shoes, the works. Crazy thing is I liked it. My father called me a 'fegele,' you know what that means? I said 'Look Pop, I like girls. I ain't no fag.'

"All the guys in the neighborhood called me a fruit or a fag because of the dancing. I had to learn to fight. One by one I beat up every kid on our block, the dancing helped. After I knocked them down I'd help them up and say 'I'm sorry I had to beat you up but stop calling me a fag.' My old man said 'Why do you have to help them up and apologize, it proves you're a fag.'

"My mother was right, I danced in a lot of shows, *Oklahoma* is one. Did you know it was called *Away We Go* out of town and was a bomb? I made a lot of money for the family, more money than the old man ever made. But then I got too old to hoof and I started hackin'. I got married and had six kids, all grown. I'm crazy about my wife and we have a good life.

"My father still calls me a 'fegele' but what the fuck does he know?"

Dylan

My friend Andrew Ciesielski lives behind the White Horse Tavern. The White Horse, as you know, was once the haunt of great poets and playwrights: Dylan Thomas, Delmore Schwartz and Brendan Behan; it is now the haunt of graduate student English majors— the Lit-Crit bunch. Mr. Ciesielski was passing the White Horse one holiday morning, and standing in front of the tavern was a nice-looking young man, say fifteen, clearly a tourist with a map in his hand. He was with a woman obviously his mother, say the best-dressed woman in Akron, Ohio, and his father was standing nearby smoking a pipe. Just as Mr. Ciesielski was passing, the young man pointed his finger at the White Horse and said "Now this is where Bob Dylan died." Mr. Ciesielski couldn't resist and said "No, son, Dylan Thomas and four blocks away at St. Vincent's Hospital."

The mother gave Mr. Ciesielski a look which clearly said "I'm glad it's you and not me." I suppose that's how history is rewritten.

Andy's Mother

I know no one wants to hear another word about Andy Warhol. Judging by the stack of books available at the Museum of Modern Art where there was a huge retrospective of his work not another word should be said for twenty years, but indulge me for a moment? I always thought of Andy as a Hunky from East McKeesport. East McKeesport is a Bessemer furnace away from my own hometown of Braddock, Pa., and neither of them is a garden spot. Hunkys are Slovaks, Serbs, Croats, Hungarians and the word is not pronounced honkey that's another pejorative. Hunkys are also not Polacks or Italians.

I'm reading his diaries, and it's an extraordinary experience, like salted peanuts or more to my taste salted cashews: "Just one page, then another, then another and finally you've eaten the whole bowl and

135

you suspect there hasn't been much nourishment in the process. One of the reasons for the popularity, it gives everyone a chance to be superior. I'm sure people say to themselves as I did, "Well no matter how bad I've been I've never done that or more to the point I've never taken that."

Furthermore, his life is one everyone understands: He lead the life he read about in *Photoplay* when he was twelve. The diaries are irresistible.

When Andy Warhol died *The New York Times* newspaper was somewhat ambiguous about his birthplace. I was indignant and fired off a letter to the writer of the obit saying that a few phone calls would have told him that Andy was born in East McKeesport, Pa. *The Times*, as it turned out, was right. Though he claimed to have been born in East McKeesport, he was actually born in Shadyside, an upper middle-class section of Pittsburgh. It's as though he was born in New Rochelle and pretended to be born in the south Bronx. Now that's perverse.

When I would run into Andy Warhol in the late fifties we would discuss the Pittsburgh Pirates of our youth. He was a passionate Pirate fan and if you don't believe me ask Marvin Kitman the TV critic for *Newsday* with whom Andy also discussed the Pirates. Surprise?

One of the things people forget about art is that what artists mostly do is fool around: poets fool around with words (that's Auden speaking), musicians fool around with sound and painters fool around with paint, canvas and other things. It is not always easy to tell the difference between "fooling around" and art because there isn't any but let me tell you about the fooling around and the art in the Andy Warhol retrospective.

The portrait of Truman Capote is one of the great portraits of the twentieth century, no reason even to read the Capote biography, Andy's portrait tells you all. The Mao Tse-tung room, he had a whole room to himself, looking at it was an extraordinary experience. The Philip Johnson portrait is as accurate a portrait as you will ever see—mean as cat shit is Philip Johnson. The self portrait of Andy with his fingers to his lips is wonderfully self-revealing but the real stunner is Andy's portrait of his mother Julia Warhola, everything you need to know about Andy Warhol is in that portrait. He was not fooling around when he did that. It's as serious as art gets. A portrait of a Hunky lady from East McKeesport, Pa., who had moved to Shadyside.

Vuitton

I once did a favor for a friend, Ruth Nathan. She was one of the first high-powered female movie executives. She was buying material for Universal Pictures, working for "nice guy" Stanley Newman. I gave her a tip on a book. I happened to read this hot manuscript as it was coming out of someone's typewriter so she was the first in her industry to know about it. She bought it for Universal and saved her company sixty or seventy thousand dollars. She sent me, as high-powered movie ladies did in those days, two bottles of Tattinger champagne in those little coffins with the fake red velvet lining. I know that I'm a low-class Irishman trying to be a gentleman but occasionally I slip and I ungraciously called her up and said "Two bottles of champagne in little red velvet caskets is not enough reward for what I did for you." She said: "I know Sweetie but what can I do, try and think of something you'd like."

A few months later I was lying in bed one morning still trying to think of the words to "Margie" when it hit me. I called Mrs. Nathan up and said "I know, I want a Louis Vuitton backpack." She hooted in that wonderful way of hers, said "*Formidable*," and sent me a Vuitton dustpan, *faux*, of course. I did think walking down Fifth Ave. with a Louis Vuitton backpack might freak a few people.

A few years later I was in Monte Carlo—don't get me wrong it was a business trip paid for by the company—a meeting called Distropress, international book and magazine distributors. I gave fifty dollars to our hot-shot sales manager Ed Shukin and told him to see if he could win me some bread (we talked like that in those days). He did. A lot of bread, sorry money. We're talking down payment on a house or a new car. Now as you know I'm not only a guilt-ridden Irish Catholic I'm basically a Victorian prude and puritan, I regard money won "that way" as dirty. I didn't trust myself to hold on to it until I got back and could give it to Dorothy Day so I sensibly decided to spend it. Instead of a modest little trip to Italy after business in Monte Carlo, I booked myself into the Paris Ritz for a week.

I spent a lot of time at the Ritz drinking champagne with fresh peaches, writing letters to friends on Ritz stationery and taking baths—if you press the right button in the middle of the bath someone comes in and scrubs your back—the first time I did it was an accident, but not the second.

One day I was in the Ritz elevator with two gents, this is true, one of the gentlemen turned to the other gentleman and said in French, "Excuse me sir are you Bing Crosby?" The other gentleman said in what seemed like perfect French, "But no Monsieur only wish I was" in a voice which was unmistakably Bing Crosby. The Frenchman got out of the elevator first shaking his head and just before he left the elevator Mr. Crosby turned and winked at me.

In Paris I found time to go to Louis Vuitton and said to the haughty salesman that I would like a backpack. He said "But Monsieur, we don't sell backpacks." Too bad. After a few minutes the light bulb went on over his head and he said "We would be delighted to make you a backpack. But, of course we would need a model to copy but please don't send one from Abercrombie and Fitch there might be copyright problems." Clearly he thought I was the sort of person who shopped regularly at Abercrombie and Fitch when in truth, except for this fling I shopped for such things at Army surplus. The Vuitton backpack was going to cost several thousand dollars and Universal Pictures was not going to pay for it so I forgot about it and went to Cartier and bought some luggage—they had just come out with a new line. It was called Le Must and I couldn't even pronounce it but I could pay for it. When the haughty Cartier salesman said "Where should we deliver it?" I said "Send it to my hotel—THE RITZ."

My youngest sister had behaved so splendidly during the terminal illness of my father that after he died I went right into Saks Fifth Avenue, plunked down the money and bought her a Vuitton bag, her heart's desire. I was tempted by those guys on the street but buying your sister a fake Vuitton is not exactly a classy thing to do. Louis Vuitton finally opened up its own store on Fifty-seventh Street and like the insufferable Gucci, it closes for lunch—imagine closing for lunch in New York. I was passing the store one day at lunchtime and noticed that it was closed and also noticed that a man, a street vendor, not a Senegalese but an African-American man was selling Vuitton luggage in front of Vuitton itself. Now that's chutzpah. I'm always looking for good imitation Vuitton because my two other sisters, one in Sacramento and one in Portland, are fiercely jealous of the one in L.A. and wanted Vuitton bags of their own from their big brother—they don't know in Sacramento and Portland that Vuitton with the initials is no longer chic—so I was examining the bags when this young woman came up next to me, picked up one of the bags and said to the salesman "Is this a genuine Vuitton bag?" And the man said "Lady is you crazy? These is ripoffs." Right on, brother.

Noel

Here are two relatively unknown bits for Noel Coward's birthday. One day, in New York Mr. Coward went into Western Union to send a telegram to his best friend Gertrude Lawrence. He signed the telegram Fiorello LaGuardia. The telegraph operator said "You can't sign the name Fiorello LaGuardia, you're not Fiorello LaGuardia." Noel Coward said "Very well, old chap" and signed with his real name Noel Coward. The telegraph operator said "Are you really Noel Coward?" and Noel Coward said "Yes." "In that case" the telegraph operator said "you can sign yourself Fiorello LaGuardia."

When Gertrude Lawrence got married she got a telegram from her best friend Noel Coward and it read as follows:

Patrick O'Connor

Dear Mrs. A. hooray, hooray.
At last you are deflowered.
On this, as every other day
I love you, Noel Coward.

Christine

The death of Christine Jorgensen a pioneer woman if there ever was one who was known as George when he was in the United States Army went unremarked by many. So let's rectify that. Christine Jorgenson as you know was one of the first if not the first to have a sex change operation, and she had it in Sweden. Headlines everywhere and finally she came back to the United States and to her hometown, Los Angeles. A reporter from *The Los Angeles Times* thought it would be a good idea to find one of Christine's old Army buddies and get his point of view as Christine landed at the Los Angeles Airport. So the enterprising reporter found one of Christine's Army friends named Mike and took him to the airport on the day of her arrival. They were both standing on the runway as Christine came off the plane and on to the ramp in a picture hat, black chiffon dress, long black kid gloves and high heels. When Christine alighted the reporter turned to Mike and said "Well what do you think of your old Army buddy now?" and Mike the old army buddy said "Same old George."

Scaasi

By some fluke I get invited to Arnold Scaasi openings. He designs women's clothes and he's the hottest American designer extant. Not as hot as that Frenchman Christian something but still pretty hot. All those ladies who are in Suzy's column every day wear his clothes and they sell for up to $30,000 per dress. Well may you ask what a Trotskyite is doing at the opening of New York's most fashionable designer with the likes of Mrs. Jean MacArthur and Mrs. Hearst and Patty Hearst as well. I go because of the failure of twentieth-century art.

People used to go to the theater for pleasure, for beauty, for charm, to be entertained, to be, if you will, recreated, to have their souls refreshed. Then along came Shaw, Ibsen, Chekhov, Strindberg—that bunch and it was all over, the beginning of didactic theater, or one might say the theater of the missionaries. At some point Shaw said "There isn't a theater in London to which I can take my friend William Morris," you remember Morris, the Morris chair and all that artsy-craftsy stuff. Well from that moment on we were doomed. The American theater got into the hands of the intellectuals and anything that gets into the hands of intellectuals—governments, universities, businesses, radio stations—is doomed from the beginning.

The American theater took it up immediately and then we had the dreariness of the Group and Clifford Odets and Irwin Shaw and then Arthur Miller and their gloomy round of liberal agitprop plays—I swore I wouldn't use that word but there you are. And then the influence of the worst theater in the world, the Russian: No, we couldn't imitate the French and their boulevard theater or the English and their lovely Shaftbury Avenue charm. We had to imitate the Russians and the dreary Scandinavians. So people stopped going to the theater and with good reasons. Then they started going to the ballet. As George Balanchine said "There are no mother-in-laws in the ballet." No problems, no problem ballets, nobody trying to convert you to universal brotherhood. Just beautiful, well-trained people doing beautiful things often on tiptoe. There's no fooling around at the ballet—you can either do it or you can't—

and very little fooling around about looks—homely girls don't become ballerinas. So Americans rightly deserted the theater and took up the ballet because they knew what they were getting into.

As you know intellectuals never rest and now they've managed to infiltrate if not the ballet proper at least modern dance south of 14th Street. I've seen by actual count sixty-three ballets about the horrors of the bomb. One of the reasons choreographers are so hipped on the bomb (after the bomb, before the bomb, etc.) is that it's very difficult to do a ballet about Keynesian economics, not that some of them haven't tried.

Now I haven't given up the ballet by any means, but the new choreographers are driving me away so I go to fashion shows—that is to say to Arnold Scaasi openings where for about an hour and a half you may see the most beautiful and interesting women in the world—one of his models, a tall dark Oriental lady is so beautiful she would knock your socks off—modeling the most beautiful clothes in the world. Nothing to do but feast your eyes and give yourself up to the pleasure of the experience. As they come down the runway in their laces and satins and feathers and silks the audience, or at least this audience, is transported to another land, a land of instinctive poise as Auden said, where all things are beautiful and wonderful and of an infi-

149

nite possibility. In other words pleasure for the mind and spirit.

My contention is that this is the kind of pleasure one used to have at the theater: ecstatically beautiful women, women essentially of fantasy, dressed as they might be in heaven (a decadent heaven to be sure), the vision of which refreshes the soul.

White Linen

When I was a boy in Braddock, Protestants wore white linen in the summer. Catholics wore blue and it wasn't linen. All my young life I wanted a white linen suit. It seemed the height of elegance. But I was always too cheap to indulge myself in such extravagance. Who besides Tom Wolfe wears white linen.

One day I was passing Sulka, then as now one of the most expensive men's stores in the world and they were going out of business. Always searching for a bargain I went in and there was my white linen suit— I tried it on, it fit and in a moment of rare self-indulgence I bought it. It was on sale, it had been five hundred dollars and it was on sale for less than two hundred. Though I had never paid that much for a suit in my life I thought of it as a bargain. It looked good on me and I felt good in it. I wore it to weddings and bar mitz-

vahs, graduations, garden parties and to Chinese and
Japanese funerals though there have been very few of
those. The suit gave me a great deal of pleasure.

One hot day I was standing on Riverside Drive
waiting for a bus, wearing my white suit, and there was
a sudden downpour, the heavens opened up and we had
a real summer storm. All New Yorkers know that damn
number 5 bus never comes and if you get caught in a
downpour on Riverside Drive there is no place to seek
shelter from the storm and you end up getting soaking
wet, and I did. I was on my way to some fete or another
and I was sure I would arrive at the party a sodden
mess. To my astonishment there was not a wrinkle in
my white linen suit, which seemed mysterious. When
I got home that night I tore that damn suit apart looking for the label and when I finally found one it said
one hundred percent polyester. I was outraged.

I took it back to Sulka which had by then
opened another store at a new address. I entered the
store in high dudgeon. "You sold a polyester suit and
told me it was linen what do you intend to do about
it?" Of course, I didn't have the sales slip but it was a
Sulka suit. They said "But sir, this suit is fifteen years
old." I said "What difference does it make? You sold
me a suit under false pretenses and you are either an
honorable firm or you're not, I'll sue, I'll blacken your

name." I tend to be melodramatic when my dudgeon is high.

Well of course I didn't sue and of course I didn't blacken their name until this very moment. The suit has been hanging in the closet for ten years. I still want a linen suit and what I thought I might do is have the tailor press some deep permanent creases in it or sleep in it so it looks like linen. Meanwhile If anyone wants a Sulka polyester suit let me know. Forty-two portly.

Bridge

You know how people always say "Oh, I could be a good bridge player if only I played more." Well, once on a troop ship to New Guinea I played bridge eighteen hours a day for forty-three days and I never got better. I am a passionate bridge player and I play all the time, mostly at the Culbertson Club on Fifth Ave. and Ninth St. in what used to be the Fifth Avenue Hotel. It's run by a nice guy named Ron McConnel. I bid with great authority and slam those cards on the table like Ely Culbertson, never hesitating for a moment over a bid or a play. When you play duplicate bridge which I do at the club you only play with an opposing pair for two or at most five hands at a time so because of my bidding authority and swift play people think I'm terrific and when I make a truly stupid error which I often do my opponents chalk it up to a bad night or some such. One night I made such an egregious error that my opponent kindly said "You probably pulled the wrong card." I hadn't.

One day a lady named Dorinda Schaffer came up and whispered something in my ear. Now Miss Schaffer is a very genteel Southern lady not to say gentlewoman with exquisite manners and what she said to me was "You may fool the others but you don't fool me you are a damn lousy bridge player and you're holding your partner back and if he ever played with a decent player he might get to be pretty good." With that she thrust an elementary bridge book in my hand and said "Study." My own attitude about the South is that if they had sent the women to the Civil War instead of those moonshine-swilling sissies, they would have won. My friend and critic Dorinda represents the best of Southern womanhood. I studied but it didn't do any good.

A few weeks after this incident there was a national bridge tournament at the Javits Center and I hadn't seen the Javits Center and it was raining so I convinced my partner that we should enter. No qualifications necessary just pay your entrance fee and you're in. When my partner and I showed up our friends from the Culbertson Club were there and Dorinda said "Patrick, you get out of here you can't play bridge let alone tournament bridge." But we did stay and we played and we won. When I went over and told my so-called friends they said "It must be a computer mistake." So elated were we by the win in the afternoon that we stayed for the evening and won again making us the novice winners for the entire tournament, and our names were in the bridge column of *The New York Times* newspaper the next day. Of course the people at the club thought it was some kind of fix. But it wasn't. It just proves that even a lousy bridge player occasionally gets dealt a hand he can't screw up. I still haven't improved and newcomers to the club are fooled for a few days into thinking I'm a terrific bridge player but not my friend Dorinda. She knows what a lousy player I am and just keeps shaking her head.

Chinese Food

      This is a story about some former East Germans but it is not a story about escape or repression. My best friend and his wife and two children lived in a small town in East Germany called Gera. He's a doctor and so is she. He's also a composer of operas and a jazz musician and serious rocker. He speaks all languages. He's what is called a polymath. I visited Fritz and his family in East Germany for years. Finally after years of being harassed by East German border guards and train guards and sick of bureaucrats at the Fredrichstrasse subway station and Checkpoint Charlie, I said to Fritz "Let's meet somewhere else for vacation." It used to drive me up the wall when people said to me "Why don't you meet your friends somewhere nice like Paris?" Most people didn't have a clue until recently that freedom to travel was the main issue.

Traveling for East Germans for the past twenty years was like playing Chinese checkers, sometimes they could go to Poland, sometimes to Czechoslovakia. Always Bulgaria and Rumania and never to Hungary or Yugoslavia. For years I had been telling Fritz and his wife Martine about the glories of Chinese food. Finally, a Chinese restaurant opened in Prague and I said we'll meet in Prague and fortunately that year Prague was open to East Germans—unfortunately it was just a year after the Russian invasion. I made a reservation by mail six months in advance, I called innumerable times from New York, not an easy task and finally the great day arrived: Fritz, Martine and I presented ourselves at the only Chinese restaurant in Eastern Europe. We were turned away. As usual, we were bumped by Russian generals. For forty years in Eastern Europe one was always being bumped by Russian generals. The next year I made the same reservations at the same Prague Chinese restaurant, this time through friends at the Czech embassy in New York, called several times from New York, called the day before in Prague, arrived at the restaurant and once again were turned away. We tried three years running and were always bumped by some damn Russians.

Finally I heard about a Chinese restaurant opening up in Warsaw and I said, "Next year we meet in

Warsaw." And we did. I took all the precautions: made reservations through a friend in the Polish embassy in New York, called from New York, again no easy task, called when I got there and took a special precaution, went myself to the restaurant on the morning of the reservation and bribed the maitre d'. We presented ourselves, Fritz speaks perfect Polish. The restaurant was divine: red lacquer everywhere, dragons everywhere, shiny black tables. Perfect. I ordered. After a few bites Fritz looked at me and said "Patrick is this really Chinese food?" It was sauerkraut with soy sauce.

Anti-Semitism
on the West Side

In the late seventies I was living quite com-
fortably on the Upper West Side with all the things that
make a New Yorker's life pleasant: a rent-controlled
apartment, a psychoanalyst who understood me, a decent
barber and an efficient dry cleaner who didn't require
that I hold on to the ticket.

After a time I began to perceive that the owner
of the dry cleaning establishment who I'll call Seymour
didn't like me. Now I'm as paranoid as the next New
Yorker and that's what I chalked it up to—paranoia. I
couldn't think of anything I had done to offend Seymour
so I just continued giving him my business. Finally he
told me he didn't want my business and I thought of
the immortal words of Delmore Schwartz "Even para-
noids have enemies." I told Seymour he had to take my
business, it was the law. On the day of the Jim Jones/Kool

Aid massacre Seymour said to me, "It's people like you who cause situations like that." Now you may wonder why I stayed with Seymour and I'll tell you. Aside from the fact that he was a good and efficient dry cleaner and I didn't need to hold on to my ticket, massive rejection of that kind when there is no apparent reason for it is wonderful material for the analyst's couch. I then began to get an inkling of the trouble, Seymour perceived me as an anti-Semite. The irony of it all was that unlike most of my Jewish friends on the Upper West Side I am pro-Israel and an active Zionist but I never told this to Seymour.

Often I would arrive at the dry cleaners on Friday evening overburdened with a brief case and a tote bag filled with manuscripts for weekend reading and try to pick up my dry cleaning and shirts instead of going in on Saturday morning empty handed like a noncompulsive person. I was not the only compulsive New Yorker who did this. So Seymour had these nice bright Puerto Rican high school boys who for a buck or two would help you home with your cleaning and packages of shirts.

One Friday evening Angel, one of the nicest and brightest, was helping me home with my stuff and he asked me why I didn't tell Seymour my real name which as you know is Patrick O'Connor. I said it just wasn't worth the trouble. Months earlier Angel had asked me why Seymour called me Pat O'Brien instead of Pat O'Connor and I had said to Angel, "You know how Jews are, they think all Irishmen are called Pat O'Brien." Angel said "I told Seymour what you said and he got mad." So that was it. Finally I knew that because I said the word Jew in that way Seymour perceived me as a virulent anti-Semite. Now that I knew I felt lots better but I didn't do anything to disabuse Seymour of his notion.

Some months later I was having lunch at the Drake Hotel with General Mordecai Gur, head of the Israeli Army. People in the book business will understand but others may need an explanation. Editors, even lowly ones, have lunch with all sorts of people. I have a friend, who though she is not a lowly editor, regularly dined with Nancy Reagan because they were working on her book. Though lunch with Mrs. Reagan is not my idea of heaven. I was editing General Gur's book about the six-day war and we lunched together many times both in New York and in Israel. In addition he is a well-known writer of children's books.

I said to him "Mota," I called him Mota. "Hurry up and eat your lunch you have to do me a favor. And you can't have any dessert, you're too fat as it is, how do you expect to look like a hero and raise money for

Israel if you look like someone's brother-in-law who comes over on Saturday night to do the taxes." He finished his lunch, we got in a cab and went to the Upper West Side to Seymour's dry cleaning establishment. Now Seymour was a big Zionist and I knew he would know the face of the head of the Israeli army. As we walked in I said "Seymour I want you to meet my friend General Gur." Seymour was speechless. He turned ashen and when he recovered he asked General Gur for his autograph. From that day forward I was treated by my dry cleaner with the respect you can imagine a Zionist would give to the best friend of the head of the Israeli Army even if his name was Pat O'Brien.

Brooks Brothers

I know that it's politically incorrect to talk about Brooks Brothers but I have a politically incorrect past so here goes. Eighteen years ago for my fiftieth birthday my friend Bill Koshland gave me a splendid party. My friends gave me lots of gift certificates to Brooks Brothers. I must have been going through my Brooks Brothers phase. I have since gone through a Paul Stuart phase, a Turnbull Asser phase and now I'm going through my thrift-shop phase. As my analyst might say perverse till the end.

I wanted a black blazer and manufacturers don't make black blazers or didn't then, and I couldn't figure out why. I used the gift certificates and had one made for the astonishing price of five hundred and fifty dollars. The first day I wore it I discovered why men don't wear black blazers. When you wear it no matter where you are, be it on the beach or on the subway plat-form, someone will come up to you and say "Is my table ready?" Nothing daunted I wore it for fifteen years and eventually it looked like it was ready for the rag-bag but now that I'm in my thrift-shop mode it didn't matter. I was wearing the blazer one day while passing Brooks Brothers and decided what the hell I'd go in and see what they had to say, they can only throw me out. I went up to the custom department looking like a raggle-taggle gypsy, took the blazer off and asked the man if anything could be done with it. He never bat-ted an eye. He took the blazer from me and said he would see. I went back to Vermont and forgot about it. Last Thursday I was back in town—the ski season is over—remembered finally where I had left the jacket, went back to Brooks. The man handed me my jacket. It looked as good as new. The lining had been fixed, it had new silver buckles. It was fabulous, like a magic coat. I was truly afraid to ask how much but I did. "No charge sir." So if you need to have faith in something try Brooks Brothers. People still come up to me and ask "Is my table ready?"

Ray Charles

Two years ago I went to Taos, New Mexico, to ski. The altitude at Taos is too high for someone with a bad heart but I toughed it out. I also found a new way to indicate the difficulties of a ski slope: instead of green circle, red circle and black diamond for most difficult, I thought of the slopes as one nitro-, two nitro- and three nitro-glycerin tablets. After a week of a very rugged ski school I had a bad sunburn, altitude sickness and I was totally exhausted. On the Saturday night before Easter I went to Albuquerque so I could get an early plane to New York on Sunday morning. Spent the night with friends and since we hadn't seen each other for some time we stayed up all night talking so that by the time I got to the airport I was a basket case.

The Albuquerque airport on Easter Sunday morning seemed not just deserted but abandoned. I was walking down one of the eerily empty corridors when I saw sitting against the wall Ray Charles in silver robes with golden tablets in his lap.

Years ago in Israel I was being driven down a dusty road—all roads in Israel are dusty—when we came across a small river, to call it a rivulet would be pretentious. I asked the driver what it was and he said "The River Jordan." I made him stop the car, I got out, rolled up my pant legs, took off my shoes and socks and waded in. The Arab driver clearly thought I was crazy. Then I said to myself, "Why not?" I scooped up some water with my hand, sprinkled it on my head, made the sign of the cross and said in an uncharacteristically loud voice: "I baptize thee in the name of the Father, Son and Holy Ghost," except the voice that came out was not my voice but the voice of Ray Charles, the voice that sings "Georgia on My Mind." I said to myself why are you talking like that. You're not Ray Charles, you're not even black. The Arab driver didn't understand, and I did only vaguely, that the River Jordan, baptism, and God, for that matter, speak in a black voice.

So there I was in the lonely corridors of the Albuquerque airport on Easter Sunday morning staring at the man himself, Ray Charles, in silver robes with golden tablets in his lap. I began to cry. I went up

to him and said "Mr. Charles?" and he said in that "Fool
For Love" voice "Yes, son." I said "Mr. Charles, may
I hold your hand?" he said, "Why, yes, son." And there
I was, tears streaming down my face holding Ray
Charles's hand. Neither of us said anything. I wasn't
embarrassed about the crying, after all, Ray Charles
couldn't see me. I could see out of the corner of my
tear-filled eye his factotum arranging something at the
ticket counter. In a few minutes the man came over,
collected Mr. Charles and the two of them marched
down to the boarding gate at the stately tread of the
Archbishop of Canterbury. I followed in their wake, a
willing acolyte thinking no plane that has Ray Charles
on board could possibly crash.

　　　　It really was Ray Charles: The silver robes were
a silver-colored raincoat, the golden tablets were a mus-
tard-colored book in braille or perhaps a magazine.
When I called my Albuquerque friends from the boarding gate to tell them that I had just spent the last ten
minutes holding Ray Charles's hand they said "Get
some sleep." And on the plane I slept the sleep the just
might sleep in the divine presence.

Odd Couple

I noticed an odd couple in the locker room. The older man was in his forties, working man, tough, not a body builder but with a body made of copper wire, strong but flexible, I had seen him give himself brutally punishing workouts on the mats of the third floor. The other was maybe sixteen, homely and goofy-looking and enormously attractive in the way of homely and goofy-looking sixteen year olds. They were excited with the excitement of a new adventure, they both had new gym clothes, new sneakers, they were talking about how much everything cost but in some sense they seemed like strangers to each other. I couldn't figure them out, an odd couple indeed. Later I saw them downstairs in the workout room. The older one was clearly a fight trainer and he thought this kid was a likely prospect and he was teaching the kid to use the

punching bag after a fairly vigorous warm up. I read
the newspaper while on the stationary bicycle and I
watched them out of the corner of my eye for the next
couple of weeks. It was obvious to me after five minutes that even Cus D'Amato couldn't teach this kid to
fight his way out of a paper bag.

After a few weeks the odd couple gave up the
boxing instruction and concentrated on working out
and karate. They had obviously new karate suits and
they threw each other around on the mats for an hour.
The truth is it was the older one who threw the younger
around but he was tough and tender, sympathetic, under-
standing and compassionate. The younger just looked
at the older one in that goofy way and couldn't wait for
the whole experience to be over.

One day the older man was alone in the locker room and I asked him "How's your pupil coming?"
He said "He's no pupil, he's my son. (The possibility
of their being father and son had never occurred to me.)
I'm trying to teach him to take care of himself. Those
streets are mean out there and he couldn't defend himself against a wet noodle. I'm not trying to turn him
into a killer or a bully I'm just trying to help out a little. He lives with his mother."

I didn't hear the rest of what he had to say, I
was holding on to the locker door so I wouldn't faint.

I was dizzy because I had never breathed in pure essence before, the essence of my life. Everything else was stripped away. I knew at that moment what my life was about. It was about the yearning to be taught by a benevolent male teacher how to physically defend myself on the mean streets of life. The sorrow and regret of its never having happened was outweighed by the enormous comfort of knowing finally the unvarnished and unambiguous truth.

C O L O P H O N

The text was set in Times New Roman, a typeface designed by
Stanley Morison (1889-1967). This face designed for *The Times*
of London was the result of a criticism Morison made to the management of *The Times* complaining of the paper's typography. They
asked him to improve it. Working for the Monotype Corporation,
Morison designed a face based on Granjon, and delivered it for use
beginning in 1932. It has since become one of the most widely
used faces and often copied because of its readability.

Composed by Olson Typographic, Brewster, New York.

The book was printed by the Haddon Craftsmen, Scranton,
Pennsylvania on acid free paper.

The first twenty-seven copies of this edition are lettered.